Mechanised Warfare in Colour

TANKS

and other
Armoured Fighting Vehicles
1900 to 1918

by
B. T. WHITE

illustrated by
JOHN WOOD

Michael Baber
Norman Dinnage
William Hobson
Alan Halliday
Tony Mitchell
Allen Randall

LONDON
BLANDFORD PRESS

First published in 1970
revised edition 1974

Copyright © 1970 Blandford Press Ltd.
167 High Holborn, London WC1V 6PH

ISBN 0 7137 0686 4

For Fiona

(4 March 1964—7 January 1968)

Colour section printed by Colour Reproduction Ltd, Billericay
Text printed in Great Britain by
Richard Clay (The Chaucer Press) Ltd, Bungay, Suffolk

PREFACE

The drawings in this book are based as far as possible on contemporary information. The colours, however, depend on such meagre written facts as exist: no colour photographs are of course available, and such paintings as are relevant cannot necessarily be guaranteed to be accurate. 'Standard' colour schemes did exist in some countries but it is clear from black-and-white photographs that these were not strictly adhered to.

A selection of the vehicles shown in the coloured drawings is also shown in cross-sectional views. Simms' Motor War Car of 1902 provides a contrast with the Austin of 1917–18—a typical armoured car of the First World War. The changes in mechanical layout of the externally similar British tanks can also be contrasted with typical French and German vehicles.

The author wishes to record his thanks to all his many friends who share his interest in the history of armoured vehicles and who, over the years, have greatly enriched his knowledge of the subject.

In connection with this particular volume, special mention should be made of Colonel Robert J. Icks, who has provided help, most generously, from his enormous fund of information on armoured vehicles.

Grateful thanks are also due to the Curator of the Royal Armoured Corps Tank Museum at Bovington in Dorset for his helpful co-operation.

B. T. WHITE

v

INTRODUCTION

The beginning of the twentieth century has been taken as a convenient starting point for this volume for several reasons.

Mechanically propelled armoured road vehicles were employed in a battle campaign for the first time in the year 1900. These machines—the Fowler armoured road locomotives employed in South Africa—turned out to be a dead end in the development of the armoured fighting vehicle but also, at the turn of the century, the earliest designs for petrol-engined fighting vehicles were being created, although these were not developed into fully armoured vehicles until a little later.

The potential of mechanical power for military use in the field was realized almost at the birth of the steam road vehicle itself, because James Cugnot offered his second steam carriage of 1770 to the French authorities as an artillery tractor. The steam vehicle itself was far too unreliable at this stage for any form of locomotion, whether civil or military, but some eighty years later, steam traction engines were able to be put to use in the Crimean War.

Probably the first armoured fighting vehicle—by modern definition—to be built was designed in 1861 by Charles S. Dickinson, a Confederate supporter in the American Civil War, and consisted of a cannon mounted on a partly armoured steam carriage. This pioneer vehicle was captured by the Federal forces before it could be tried out in action. An Italian engineer in 1854, and no less a personage than the Kaiser Wilhelm in Germany in 1897, also both designed armed and armoured steam vehicles, although neither was built. Then came the British Army Fowler armoured road trains of 1900, which introduce the illustrations in this book.

Petrol-engined vehicles mounted with a machine-gun were designed two years before the turn of the century both by Frederick R. Simms in England and Colonel R. P. Davidson in the United States. Neither were armoured (except for a shield for the gun) but these vehicles really contributed more to the ancestry of the armoured fighting vehicle than did the armoured steam locomotives. The successful, and comparatively rapid, development of the internal combustion engine following its invention in 1886 by Gottlieb Daimler led to its adoption for fighting vehicles almost to the exclusion of steam after 1900. Colonel Davidson followed up his petrol-engined vehicle with a compact steam-driven machine-gun car in 1900 which gave some indication of what might have been done had steam and not petrol engines been the main line of development of road vehicles. Davidson's 1900 vehicle is not included here because, like the 1898 machine-gun cars, it was unarmoured except for a gun shield. This officer was the leading pioneer of the fighting vehicle in the United States and his Cadillac armoured car of 1915 is shown in this book.

F. R. Simms followed up his 'quadricycle' machine-gun vehicle with a fully armoured 'Motor War Car' in 1902—a vehicle which probably derived some of its inspiration from drawings made by E. J. Pennington in 1896. A Charron, Girardot et Voigt semi-armoured automitrailleuse (machine-gun car) was exhibited at the Paris Motor Show in 1902 and this vehicle, as well as Simm's Motor War Car, attracted the wide interest of the press and helped to encourage the further development of such vehicles.

The British War Office gave no support to Simms but the French military authorities encouraged the C.G.V. firm to build an improved vehicle. This appeared in 1904, at the same time as the Austro-Daimler armoured car built in Vienna. These two fully-armoured and turreted cars must share the credit for anticipating the layout of the essentials of the armoured car in its commonest form for the next twenty years (and, indeed, in some of today's designs). Not all subsequent vehicles were fully armoured, however—the Hotchkiss of 1909 was similar to the first (1902) C.G.V., and Colonel Davidson's machine-gun cars of 1909–10 were armoured, at the most, with a gun shield.

These early fighting vehicles were armed with nothing larger than a machine-gun but the earliest armoured vehicle with a heavier weapon, the Ehrhardt of 1906 with a 5-cm. gun, coincided with the emergence of a new factor in warfare—the airship. Capable of ground and anti-aircraft fire, the Ehrhardt was followed by other vehicles in both Germany and the United States equipped with A.A. guns, although these were not in every case armoured. The 1909 Daimler mounted with a 5·7-cm. gun was, however, fairly well armoured and the gun, unlike that of the 1906 Ehrhardt, was capable of all-round traverse.

Italy produced a few experimental armoured cars in 1911–12 and she was the first country to use armoured fighting cars in a campaign—that against the Turks in Libya.

Most of the experimental armoured vehicles built in the years between 1900 and 1914 were based on ordinary passenger car or commercial chassis and they were, as a consequence, largely road-bound or confined to good hard surfaces. The need for a fighting vehicle which could leave the roads and operate cross-country was not entirely overlooked, however. The 1904 Austro-Daimler was unusual for its time in having four-wheel drive, so its performance off roads should have been better than that of its contemporaries. Another approach to the problem was typified by the adaptation as an armoured vehicle of the Ivel agricultural tractor—with large studded wheels to give good traction on poor surfaces. The Armstrong-Whitworth car of 1906 had a powered winch to haul itself out of trouble and the French Charron of 1904 carried folding bridge channels to enable it to cross small ditches.

Despite the fairly widespread and quite varied research into armoured vehicles that had been carried out in Europe and in the United States, the Russian Imperial Government was alone in fully recognizing the value of the armoured car. Although local manufacturing resources were limited, Russia acquired numbers of armoured cars from foreign countries and was the only nation to have a quantity already in service when the First World War broke out in 1914.

The Belgians were probably the first

to use motor vehicles offensively in the War—fast touring cars were employed to carry riflemen in lightning hit-and-run attacks on the advancing German Army. British cars of the Royal Naval Air Service aeroplane squadron based at Dunkirk were used in much the same way.

Both the British and the Belgian vehicles led, within a matter of weeks, to the evolution of armoured cars, firstly through the attachment of improvised armour, and then through more carefully thought out designs. By early 1915, turreted versions of the armoured cars had been produced. In France, unarmoured machine-gun automobiles designed by Captain Gentry were experimented with actively from 1906 onwards and three such cars were used in manoeuvres in Morocco in 1910; but, like the other combatants on the Western Front, no armoured cars were in French service at the beginning of August 1914. During that month, 136 armoured cars were ordered to be fitted with improvised armour—*blindage de fortune*.

In Britain, France, and Belgium, a similar policy was adopted of using powerful automobile chassis of standard design although, in most cases, the suspension was found to require strengthening to take the extra load imposed by the armour plate. All three countries equipped these cars with machine-guns, and the French and Belgians, although not the British, also had a proportion fitted with 37-mm. cannon.

Heavy armoured cars, intended originally to support the light armoured cars, were produced in 1915 on commercial vehicle chassis by Britain and

France. These had a quick-firing gun of 47-mm. calibre. The 2-pdr. (40-mm.) automatic shell-firing gun was also fitted on some British armoured cars (based on commercial chassis) for anti-aircraft use and the Russians purchased some foreign cars equipped with this weapon.

Although armoured cars could be used on the Eastern Front, as far as climatic conditions allowed, throughout the war on the Western Front the opportunities for the employment of armoured cars grew less and less as the German advance was halted and both sides dug opposing trench systems. With the perfection of these fortifications and the churning up of roads by constant artillery bombardment, the whole area near the front lines became largely impassable for wheeled vehicles. The light armoured cars were used little after the Winter of 1914-15, although the heavy armoured cars with their guns of longer range continued in limited employment, but as a form of mobile light artillery rather than in their original role of support to the light armoured cars.

These conditions of static warfare in which the trench systems were protected by barbed wire entanglements and supported by machine-gun emplacements, made infantry attacks very costly in casualties and more often than not abortive. The British Army alone suffered over 280,000 casualties in 1915.

It became increasingly clear to many that a new approach was required to break the stalemate of trench warfare. The use of artillery to support the advance was stepped up and new methods for its use—the 'creeping barrage' for example—were devised.

3

At the same time, several suggestions were put forward for cross-country armoured vehicles capable of traversing ground broken up by shell fire, cutting through barbed wire and crossing trench systems and so helping to press through successfully the infantry attack.

It is impossible to decide satisfactorily who first suggested the idea of what ultimately became the tank, because the concept itself was very old, and the same basic proposals were put forward at around the same time, quite independently, in several countries.

Without examining the contending claims, it is sufficient to say that official experiments were started early in 1915 in both the United Kingdom and in France, with no exchange of ideas between the Allies. In England, the research was undertaken under the aegis of the Admiralty and followed on, fairly naturally, from the earlier development by the Royal Naval Air Service of armoured cars, the use of which had been curtailed by the changed conditions in Flanders.

Mechanically the lines of research to produce an armoured vehicle to overcome wire, trenches, and machine-guns, soon resolved into two main types—the 'big-wheel' vehicle and the tracked vehicle. For the former, wheels of very large diameter were needed to overcome the rolling resistance in covering rough ground, to surmount vertical obstacles, to overhang wire entanglements, and to avoid dropping into small trenches. Vehicles with wheels going some way towards the size required had been built in the past —some Fowler traction engines in the late nineteenth century with 14-ft. wheels, for example.

A mock-up of a big wheel 'landship' (as the armoured cross-country machines were known as in England, because of their development by the Admiralty), with 15-ft diameter wheels, was built in England and some experiments were carried out in France with a large-wheeled tractor. It was decided in both countries that a big-wheel vehicle was impractical, besides being very vulnerable to artillery fire, although the Russians, who independently commenced building in 1915 a big-wheel machine with 9-metre diameter wheels, went on to complete it in 1917 when, after tests, it was found to be unsatisfactory.

Machines built on the 'endless track' or 'endless railway' principle were the other main alternative for a cross-country armoured vehicle and experiments became concentrated on this type in both Britain and France. The endless track itself had been developed mainly in England and the United States from the late eighteenth century onwards and by 1914 had reached such a stage that quite early in the conflict tracked machines were in use as artillery tractors. The best of these were Holt Caterpillars—American-built machines derived from earlier British patents for Hornsby-Ackroyd tractors —and they provided at least some of the inspiration for the British landships and formed the actual mechanical basis of the French tanks and later, the German A7V.

Reverting to conventional (wheeled) armoured cars, the lack of opportunities for their use on the Western Front gave the incentive to find employment for them elsewhere. The Russians remained the greatest users of this weapon and both the British and the Belgians in 1915 sent armoured car forces to support their allies on the Eastern Front. The Royal Naval Air Service Armoured Car Division, expanded by mid-1915 into nineteen active squadrons (although some were equipped only with motor-cycle combinations with machine-guns), sent units during the year to Egypt, South-West Africa, East Africa, and Gallipoli. The main equipment of the R.N.A.S. armoured car squadrons was by now confined to Rolls-Royce or Lanchester armoured cars with some Seabrook and, later, Pierce-Arrow heavy armoured cars (based, like many others built by or for the Allies, on American commercial chassis) for more specialized tasks.

Few armoured car designs of the First World War departed from features already tried out in civilian private cars or commercial vehicles, and the only really revolutionary type was the Sizaire-Berwick 'Wind Waggon', an experimental, propeller-driven armoured car. Germany was the only country to make fairly wide use of armoured cars with four-wheel drive, although the United States did supply to Britain a quantity of Jeffery-Quad 4 × 4 armoured cars. More common was the use of duplicate driving controls to facilitate getting out of difficult situations.

In both India and Ireland, locally-built armoured cars were produced to help deal with internal disturbances, although in India they were also used in the country around the North-West Frontier for border defence. In England, several armoured cars were built unofficially—usually with funds provided by, or for, specific Army units—and these varied very widely in the effectiveness of their design and construction.

The development of what were known as 'landships' or *chars d'assaut* in Britain and France respectively went ahead during 1915. The French were able to utilize the Holt caterpillar design of tracks, and the Schneider and, later, the Saint Chamond vehicles both used this type of suspension. In Britain, on the other hand, although Holt Caterpillar tractors were in use with the British Army for artillery towing, the War Office would not make any available for landship experiments. As a result, although the Holt Caterpillar was regarded as the best tracked vehicle and helped to inspire the idea of a cross-country armoured fighting vehicle, other types of commercial track systems had to be obtained for experiment—first the single, wide Pedrails and later, from America, Killen-Strait and Bullock tractors. None of these measured up to the performance required and led to the design of a new type of track by Mr W. Tritton.

British landship design was by mid-1915 following several lines of research, although the main effort was concentrated on an articulated vehicle, partly in order to achieve a reasonable degree of manoeuvrability in narrow roads of a machine of the length specified and partly because existing track systems could not satisfactorily be extended to the length required. So that an actual machine could be had for practical experiments and training by the Royal Naval Air Service, orders were given for the construction of what amounted to one half of an articulated landship equipped with Bullock tracks. This machine was known later as 'Little Willie'. The Bullock tracks were unsatisfactory and were replaced with the new type of specially designed tracks referred to above, which were very successful and widened the scope for a design less hampered by limitation on track length.

H.M. Landship 'Centipede', 'Big Willie' or 'Mother', as the vehicle was variously known, was the successful design which succeeded 'Little Willie' and used the new tracks. It was a brilliant conception, which accepted the many limitations imposed on it by the power unit available and the absence of fundamental research on many of the engineering and military problems encountered. The design ruthlessly and realistically concentrated on the essentials and 'Mother', the first true tank, was a great achievement.

'Mother' went into production in great secrecy and from this the name 'Tank' was evolved for this class of fighting vehicle, as an appropriate designation to disguise its true purpose. Unfortunately, the advantage of surprise gained was largely wasted because the Tanks, Mark I were first used in a minor offensive in September 1916 without plans or resources for exploitation. This was against the wishes of the French High Command whose tanks were not then ready for use and who perhaps more fully than the War Office realized the value of a mass surprise attack with the new weapon.

The French heavy tanks, Schneider and Saint Chamond, proved greatly inferior to the British in general effectiveness, although, theoretically at any rate, they had some advantages in the disposition of their armament and armour. Their cross-country performance was in no way comparable to that of the British tanks with their overall tracks, a design which was continued from the Mark I with little variation—except for increases in overall hull length—through successive Marks until the end of the War. This policy of introducing improvements step by step simplified the mass production of tanks by Britain, a country whose industrial capacity was already stretched with production of munitions, warships, and aeroplanes. British tanks were later supplied to the French, and to the United States Army when America entered the War.

The German heavy tank A7V had a better power/weight ratio but it shared many of the disadvantages of the Schneider and Saint Chamond tanks. Its successor A7V/U followed the layout of the British tanks, which, captured, were used more widely by the Germans than machines of their own design.

In the field of light tanks the French Renault was the only example to be produced in large numbers: it was very successful and represented the major contribution to tank development by France. The use of a standard Renault automobile engine and other well-tried components contributed to the reliability of the Renault FT 17. The German light tanks LK I and LK II went further and employed complete passenger car chassis but this did not prove to be a workable proposition.

Medium tanks, which were scaled-down equivalents of the heavies, with the same armour protection, fewer guns but a higher speed, were introduced into British service in 1918 and were intended for the exploitation role of supporting the cavalry when the enemy line was breached.

Supporting types of cross-country vehicles increased in variety as the War proceeded. Self-propelled, tracked artillery was represented by the British Gun Carrier Mark I of 1916. There were several models of French artillery of heavy calibres of up to 280 mm. on self-propelled tracked carriages, and experimental models of similar type to the French were experimented with by the United States. Two of the American S.P.C.M. are shown in this book. Obsolescent British tanks were converted into supply vehicles, and the Tank Mark V★, when introduced, was intended also as a personnel carrier. Both the supply and personnel-carrying functions were covered by the Tank Mark IX of 1918, which was specially designed for this purpose.

In the sphere of communications, for contact between tanks in battle and their headquarters, the French introduced the Char T.S.F.—a version of the Renault gun-tank equipped with radio—and a similar purpose was served by modifications to British Tanks, Mark I.

The crossing of obstacles was a major factor in the design of nearly all First World War tanks and length was one of the most important dimensions to be taken into account by tank designers. Even the 6-ton Renault with the aid of its 'tail' could cross a trench 6 ft 6 in. wide and the interesting American experimental Skeleton Tank was 25 ft long, although it weighed only 8 tons. Tail wheels were abandoned

in British tanks after their first use, but even so the trench-crossing ability of Marks II–V without tails was still about 10 ft. In standard form the Mark V★ and V★★ could cross a 14-ft gap and the projected Mark VIII★ was designed to tackle a trench of no less than 18 ft. wide. However, it was still necessary to provide auxiliary means for tanks to cross the increasingly wider obstacles dug by the enemy and fascines (later superseded by cribs), carried by ordinary British tanks, were introduced to assist in this way. The bridging of gaps up to 20 ft was to be undertaken by specially-adapted bridgelaying Tanks, Mark V★★.

Tanks contributed largely to victory for the Allies on the Western Front—the theatre of war for which they were designed—but elsewhere they were used hardly at all, although a handful of British heavy tanks was used against the Turks in 1917. Experimental tanks were produced by the Italians (the Fiat Tipo 2000 is shown here) and the Russians, although they were not used in action.

Armoured cars, however, continued in use over the main battle fronts, although in a very limited way in the West. Germany, by 1918, had over a dozen small armoured car units—each of two, or sometimes three, armoured cars. About half of these units were provided initially at any rate, with captured British, French, Italian or Russian armoured cars and the rest were equipped with German-built cars of the Ehrhardt type, which had emerged from the earlier tests as the most suitable vehicle.

The Russians made quite extensive use of armoured cars, but their most significant contribution to armoured

fighting vehicle design was the introduction of semi-tracked armoured cars
which had considerable advantages, in
typical Russian terrain, over conventional armoured cars, but without
the complication and other drawbacks
of a fully-tracked vehicle.

Armoured cars, as has been mentioned, showed in general few real
advances in design during the War.
Tanks, on the other hand, where more
fundamental problems in tracked
vehicles had to be overcome, showed a
steady, if not always spectacular, line
of mechanical improvement in the
design of power units, transmission and
steering systems, although perhaps less
attention was paid to suspension since
speeds were in most cases low. Some
refreshing (although not always successful) new approaches were shown by
American engineers in their designs in
1918.

In the United States there was also
wider appreciation of the need to
design right from the start for mass
production.

Field-Marshal Lord Kitchener was
certainly not alone in expressing
the opinion at a demonstration of
'Mother' in February 1916, that it was
a 'pretty mechanical toy'. In November
1917, after the Battle of Cambrai, in
which 476 tanks took part, few—at
least in the enemy ranks—were in
doubt as to the value of the tank. A
penetration of 10,000 yards into the
German front was made in twelve
hours—whereas an equivalent achievement at the Third Battle of Ypres,
without tanks, had taken three months.

Tanks took part in all the big battles
of 1918 and this led General Ludendorff
to report to the Reichstag on 2nd
October:

'The supreme Army Command
has been compelled to take a terribly
grave decision and declare that there
is no longer any prospect or possibility of compelling the enemy to
peace. Above all, two facts have been
decisive for this issue; first the
tanks . . . '

THE COLOURED ILLUSTRATIONS

A description of each coloured
plate is included between pages
109 and 187.

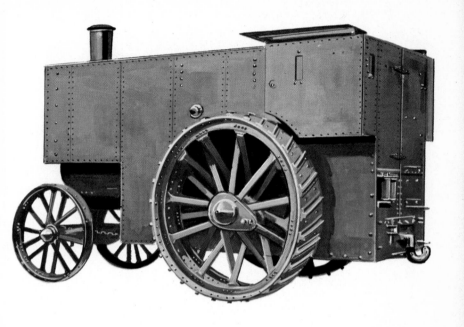

1
Fowler B.5 Armoured Road Locomotive and Armoured Road Train

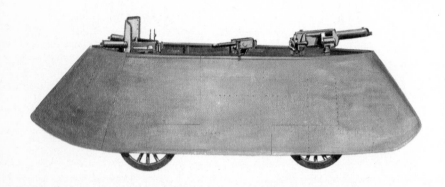

2
Simms Motor War Car

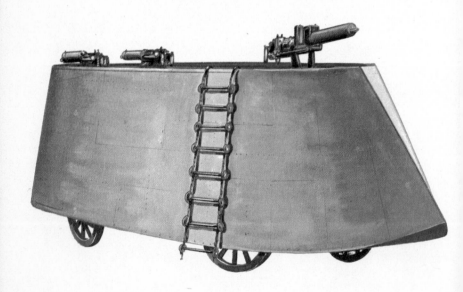

3

Automitrailleuse Charron, Girardot et Voigt

Austria—1904

4
Daimler Panzerwagen

5
Automitrailleuse Charron

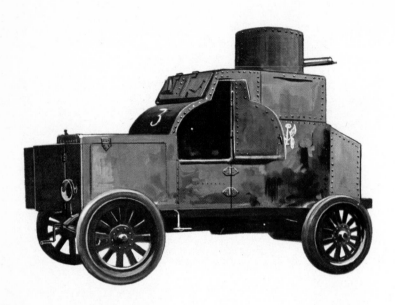

6
Armstrong-Whitworth Armoured Cars, 1906 *(below)* and 1913 *(above)*

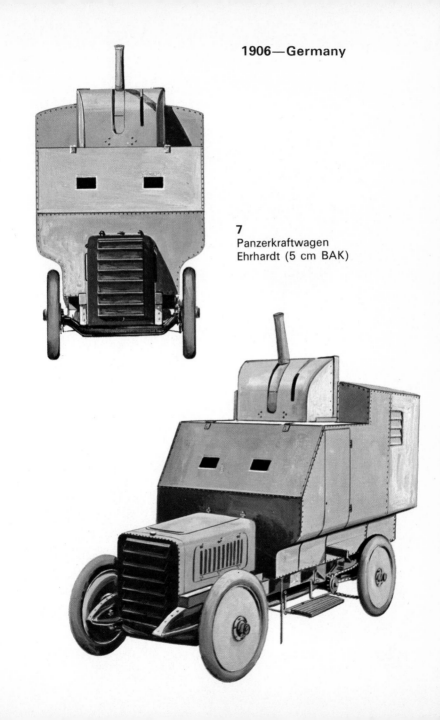

1906—Germany

7
Panzerkraftwagen
Ehrhardt (5 cm BAK)

Germany—1909

8
5·7 cm Flak auf Daimler Panzerkraftwagen

9
Automitrailleuse Hotchkiss

10
Armoured Ivel Tractor

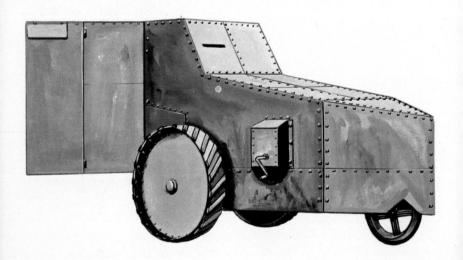

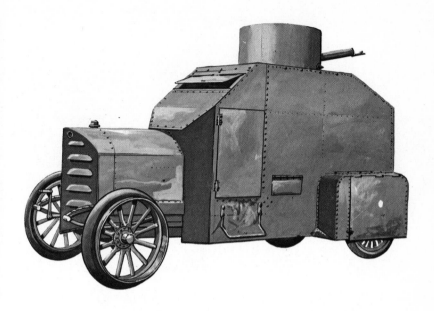

11
Automitragliatrice Isotta-Fraschini

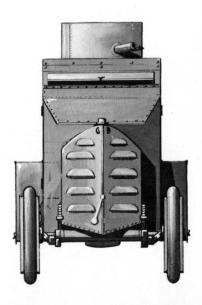

Italy—1912

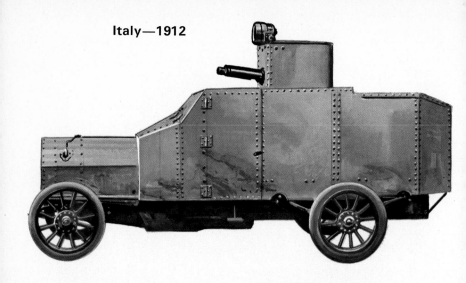

12
Autoblindata Fiat

1914—France

13
Camion Protegido Schneider

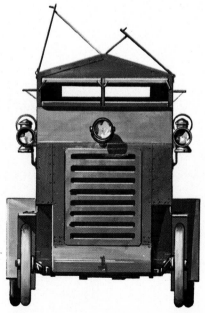

Belgium—1914

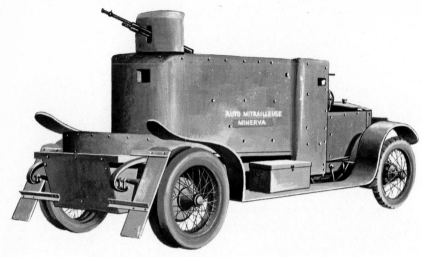

14
Automitrailleuse Minerva

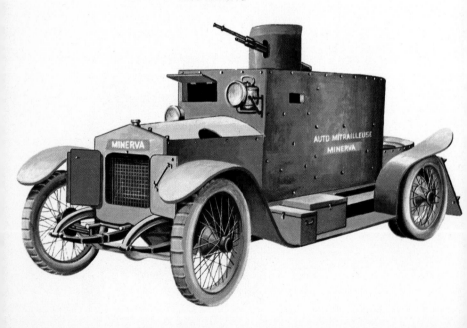

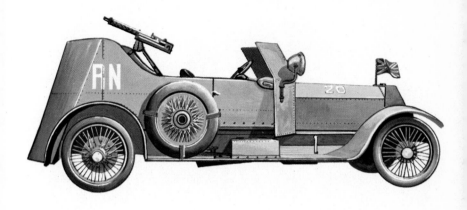

15
Armoured Car, Rolls-Royce—first R.N.A.S. pattern

16
Armoured L.G.O.C. 'B' Type chassis—R.N.A.S.

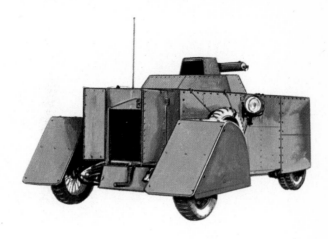

17
Armoured Car, Rolls-Royce—first Admiralty pattern *(above)*
Armoured Car, Wolseley—first Admiralty pattern *(below)*

U.K.—1914

18
Armoured Cars, Talbot—first Admiralty pattern *(above)* and modified
first Admiralty pattern *(below)*

1914—U.S.A.

19
Autocar Armoured Car

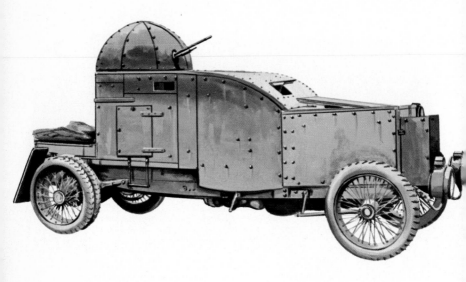

20
Automitrailleuse S.A.V.A.

21
Autocanon 37 mm, Renault

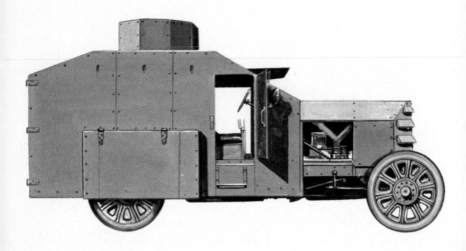

22
Isotta-Fraschini Armoured Car (built for Russia)

23
Armoured Car, Rolls-Royce—Admiralty turreted pattern

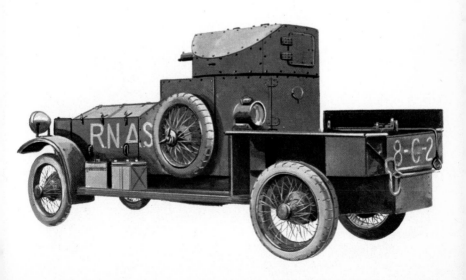

24
Packard Armoured Car

25
Armoured Cars, Isotta-Fraschini (Westmorland and Cumberland
Yeomanry), 1914 *(above)* and 1915 *(below)*

26
Armoured Car, Lanchester—Admiralty pattern

1915—Belgium

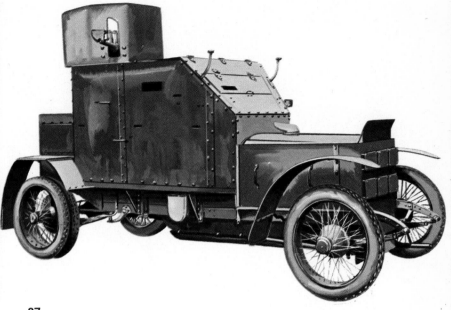

27
Autocanon Mors

28
Armoured Car, Seabrook

29
Armoured Car. A.E.C. 'B' Type—War Office pattern

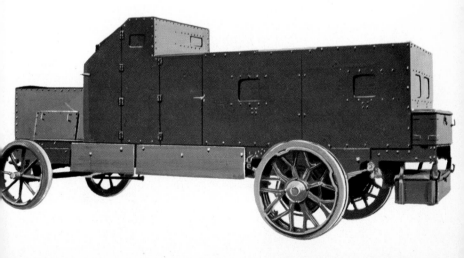

30
Armoured Car, Delaunay-Belleville—Admiralty pattern *(above*
Armoured Car, Talbot—Admiralty turreted pattern *(below)*

31
Garford Armoured Car

32
Armoured Car, Pierce-Arrow (anti-aircraft)

33
Sheffield-Simplex Armoured Car (built for Belgium)

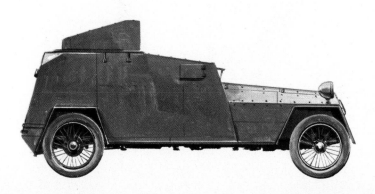

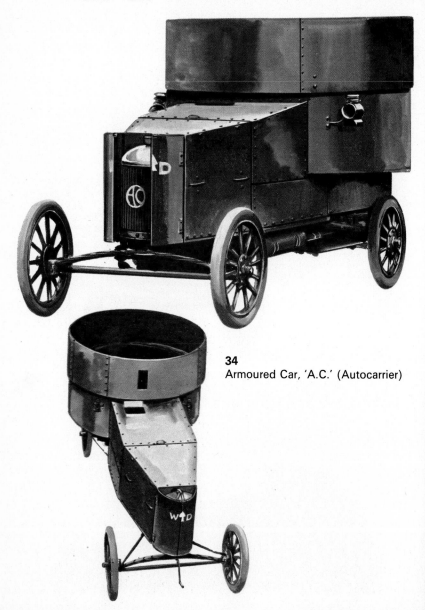

34
Armoured Car, 'A.C.' (Autocarrier)

35
Armoured Car, Cadillac—India pattern

36
Armoured Car, Fiat—India pattern (*above*)

Armoured Car (Workshop), Fiat—India pattern (*below*)

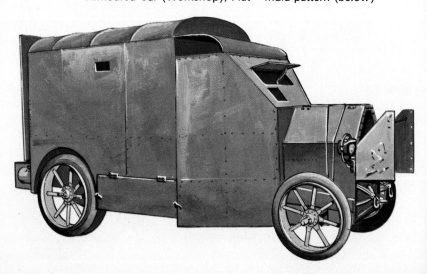

37
Armoured Car, Sizaire-Berwick ('Wind Waggon')

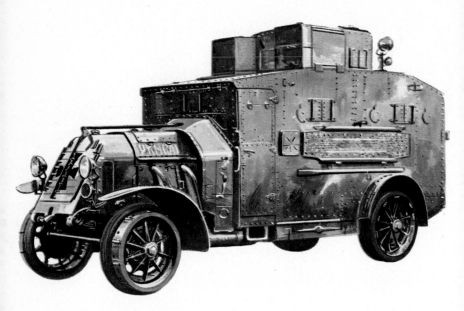

38
Panzerkraftwagen Daimler/15

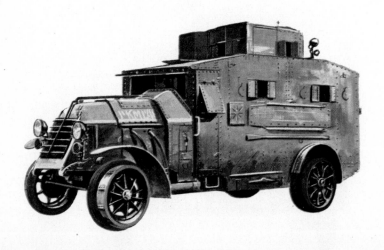

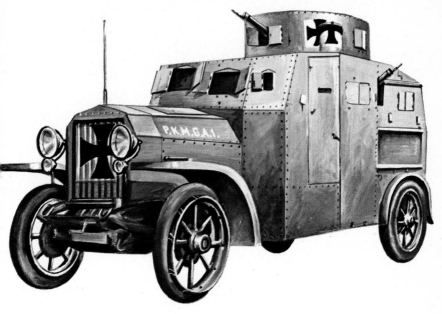

39
Panzerkraftwagen Ehrhardt/15

Germany—1915

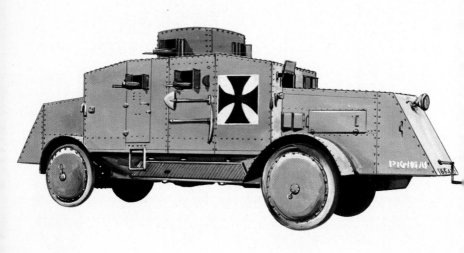

40
Panzerkraftwagen Büssing/15

41
Autoblindata Lancia 1Z

42
Davidson-Cadillac Armoured Car

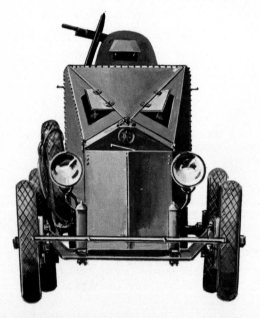

43
Austin-Putilov Armoured Car

44
Mgebrow-Renault Armoured Car

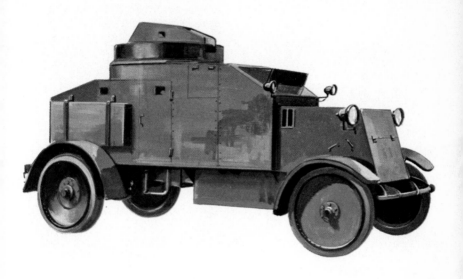

45
Armoured Car, Wolseley 'CP' Type

46
Killen-Strait Armoured Tractor

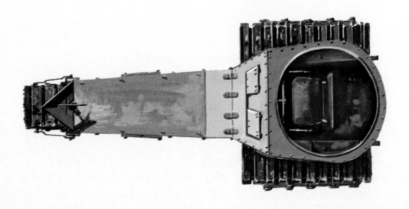

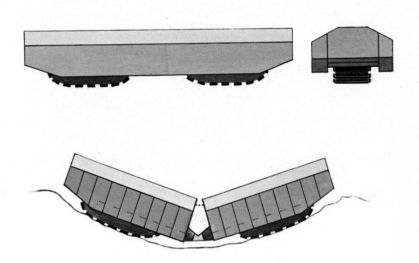

47
Pedrail Landship—original design and articulated design (*above*)
and as first completed (*below*)

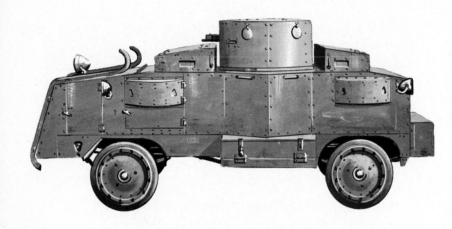

48
Armoured Car, Jeffery Quad

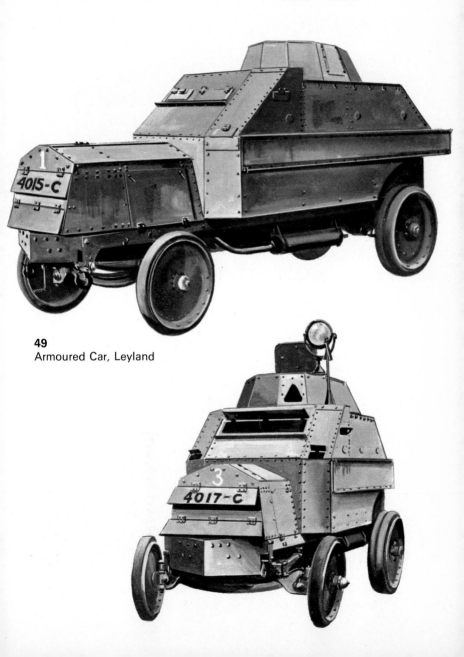

49
Armoured Car, Leyland

50
'Little Willie'

1915—France

51
Automitrailleuse White

U.K.—1916

52
'Mother'

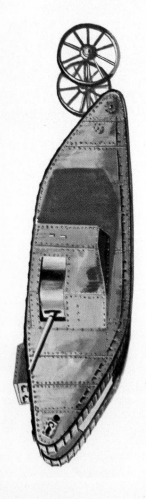

53
Sheffield-Simplex Armoured Car (built for Russia)

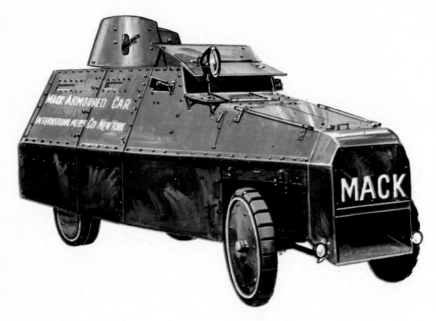

54
Mack Armoured Car (New York National Guard)

55
Fiat Armoured Car (Russia)

Ireland—1916

56
Daimler Armoured Lorry

57
Autocanon 47 mm, Renault

Germany—1916

58
Panzerkraftwagen Mannesmann-Mulag

1916—U.K.

59
Armoured Car, Mercedes-Wolseley

Italy—1916

60
Autoblindata Bianchi

61
Tank, Mark I

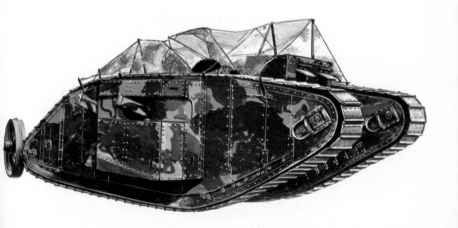

France—1916

62
Char Schneider

63
Char Saint-Chamond

64
Armoured Car, Pierce-Arrow (3pdr)

65
Packard Armoured Car (Russia)

U.S.A.—1916–17

66
King Armoured Car (*above*)   White Armoured Car (*below*)

67
Gun Carrier, Mark I

68
Armoured Car, Ford—Admiralty pattern

69
Bremer Marien-Wagen Uberpanzert (Voll Ketten)

Germany—1917

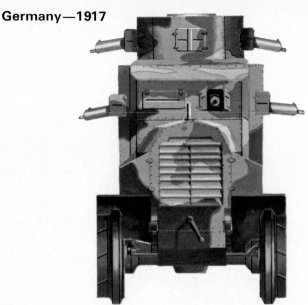

70
Panzerkraftwagen Ehrhardt/17

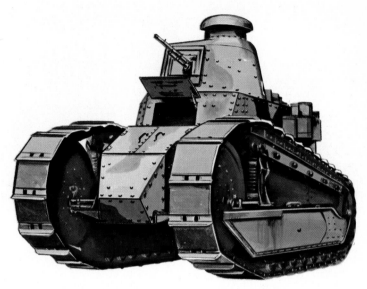

71
Char Renault FT 17

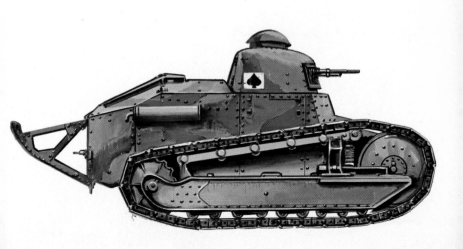

72
Austin-Putilov Half-tracked Armoured Car

73
Tank, Mark IV—'Tadpole tail' experimental model (*above*) and normal version, female (*below*)

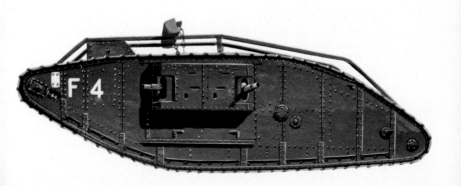

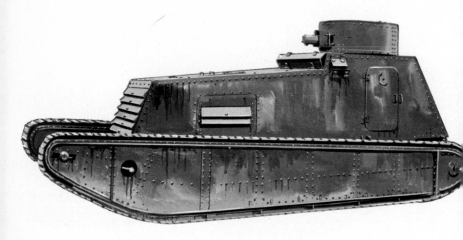

74
Leichter Kampfwagen 1

75
Tank, Medium, Mark A

Germany —1917

76
Schwerer Kampfwagen A7V

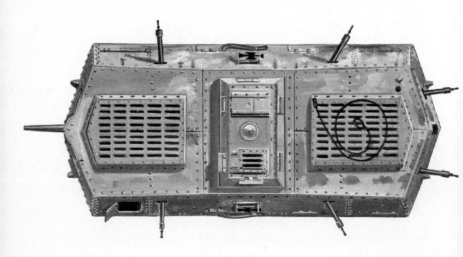

1917—France

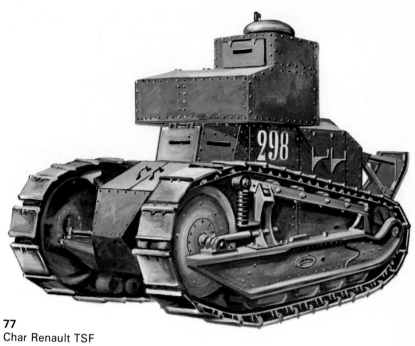

77
Char Renault TSF

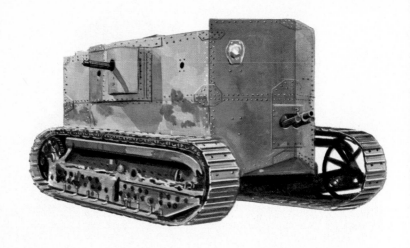

78
Holt Gas-Electric Tank

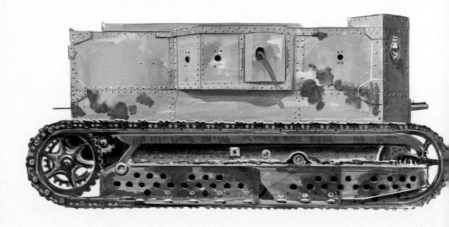

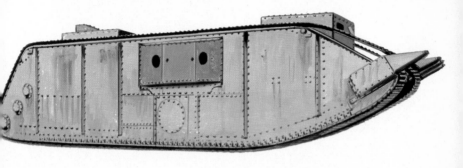

79
Steam Tank (tracked)

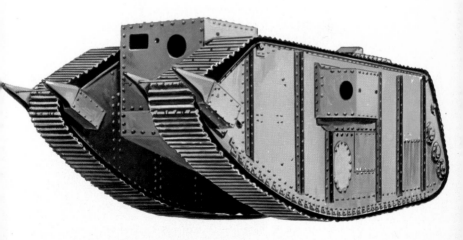

80
Armoured Car, Austin—1918 pattern

81
Tank, Mark V

Germany—1918

82
Schwerer Kampfwagen A7V/U

83
Skeleton Tank

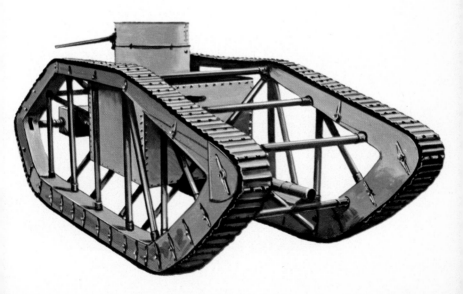

U.K.—1918

84
Tank, Mark VII

85
Tank, Mark VIII

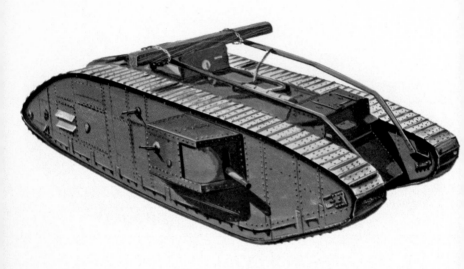

86
Tank, Mark V*—male (*above*) and female (*below*)

87
Ford 3-ton Tank

France—1918

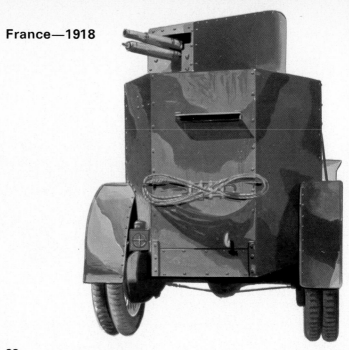

88
Autocanon Peugeot (*above*)

Automitrailleuse Peugeot, 1918 (*below*)

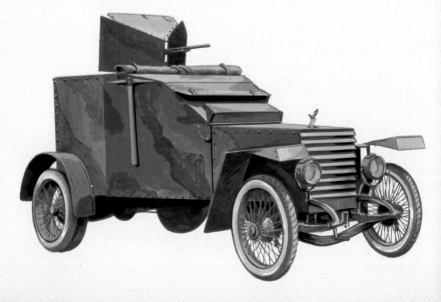

89
Leichter Kampfwagen II

90
Tank, Mark IX

1918—U.S.A.

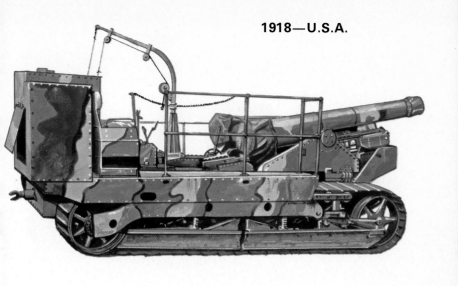

91
Self-propelled Caterpillar Mounts—Mark I (*above*) and Mark III (*below*)

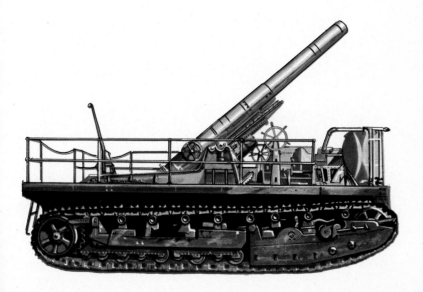

92
Tank, Medium, Mark B

93
Tank, Mark V**

94
Tank, Mark V** Bridgelayer

95
Carro Fiat Tipo 2000

96
Tank, Medium, Mark C

TANKS AND OTHER
ARMOURED FIGHTING VEHICLES

1 Fowler B.5 Armoured Road Locomotive and Armoured Road Train, 1900, U.K.

Fowler steam traction engines emerged most successfully from War Office trials in 1899 for engines to be employed in the South African war. As a consequence, machines built by John Fowler & Co. Ltd of Leeds represented by far the biggest proportion of the forty or so military traction engines that were in South Africa by mid-1900.

The traction engines were used for pulling trains of supplies—alongside oxen or mule transport—or towing guns to different positions. For protection against attacks on supply columns by Boer raiding parties some armoured traction engines were ordered, and the first of these vehicles, together with four bullet-proof trucks, arrived in South Africa in July 1900, followed by a second train two weeks later.

The armoured engines were Fowler model B.5s of 10 n.h.p. (nominal horse-power) or 115-125 maximum i.h.p. (indicated horse-power). The bullet-proof plates completely enclosed the body of the machine in a slab-sided structure, only the chimney projecting. At the front a hinged semicircular plate protected the lower part of the boiler, and at the rear the armour was extended out either side, partly over the driving wheels. Three loopholes for the use of the crew's weapons were provided in each of these projections. Access to the vehicle was by means of a door through the armour at the rear. The armoured trucks which went with the Fowler B.5s were four wheelers, the front axle, which incorporated the tow-bar, being mounted on a turntable. The armour on each side was in three sections, which could be hinged inwards independently. Each section carried a loophole. There was no overhead armour protection. A field gun could, by means of special channels, be hauled into a truck and carried, instead of being towed.

A total of four Fowler B.5s was armoured—Nos. 8894, 8895, 8898 and 8899. The first two armoured road trains were sent to Bloemfontein on arrival, where the armour was removed from both engines and trucks and used to make armoured railway trains. Towards the end of 1901 the General Officer commanding the Kimberley District asked for further trucks to be fitted with armour so that the troops needed for road-convoy escort duties could be reduced, and the War Office was requested to supply two armoured trucks. Remembering that the first two sent had been stripped of their armour to make armoured railway trains, it is not surprising that the War Office did not meet this request.

The gun-carrying truck, mentioned above, inspired Lieut.-Colonel von Layriz, a prominent German military writer, to suggest that quick-firing guns should be mounted on the wagons to act as a sort of mobile fort to protect bridges and other important points against flying columns of Boers. This idea was not adopted, but if it had it is interesting to speculate that it would have anticipated by many years some of the elements of the tank.

2 **Simms Motor War Car,** 1902, U.K.

Frederick R. Simms was a leading pioneer in England not only of the automobile itself but of fighting vehicles. A small 'quadricycle', powered by a 1½-h.p. engine, and fitted with an air-cooled Maxim machine-gun, was designed by Simms in 1898 for Vickers, Son & Maxim Ltd. This little single-seat machine was first publicly exhibited at Richmond, Surrey, in June 1899. Called the 'motor scout', the only protection of any sort—like a bicycle, it had no bodywork—was a bullet-proof shield in front of the machine-gun.

Before this, E. J. Pennington, an American, had had drawings of an armoured car of his design published in the Press. Although no vehicles of this sort seem to have been built, they appeared to have influenced F. R. Simms in the design of his 'Motor War Car' and also an armoured motor rail car. The latter was built in 1899 and sent in the following year to Nairobi, with the ultimate destination of South Africa for employment in the Boer War.

Nothing more was heard of the rail car, but the 'Motor War Car', with the same form of boat-shaped hull with rams at front and rear, was demonstrated to the Press on 4th April 1902 at the Crystal Palace in south London, where it attracted considerable interest. The design was changed in some details from the earlier drawings, because, for instance, the two turrets, each with one Maxim water-cooled machine-gun, shown in the drawings were replaced by open mountings with a 1-pdr. Maxim

quick-firing gun ('pom pom') at one end and two Maxim machine-guns at the other. These guns had shields at the Press demonstration, although at other times the shields were absent. It was claimed that alternatively a 6-pdr. gun could be mounted; or that the normal crew of four could be increased to about twelve men if the machine were required to act as an armoured personnel carrier.

The armoured hull of the Motor War Car was built by Vickers, Son & Maxim to Simms' design, whereas manufacture of the chassis was arranged by Simms' own firm. The main chassis frame was constructed of heavy U-section steel channels. The engine was carried on a sub-frame of steel tubes mounted longitudinally on the main frame. The wheels—wooden spokes and rims with steel tyres—were sprung on semi-elliptical springs at the rear and coil springs at the front. The rear wheels were of 4-ft diameter and 6-in. width, whereas the front wheels were smaller—3-ft diameter and 3½ in. wide.

The armoured 'skirt' of the hull, constructed of 6-mm. steel, was originally fixed rigidly to the tubular sub-frame, but road vibration shook the rivets loose, and so a new method of attachment was devised. The armour was mounted on semi-elliptic springs, which were fixed to the main frame by means of steel trestles, excessive movement being prevented by link arms. This 'give' also increased the effectiveness of the armour against projectiles.

The engine used was a four-cylinder (90 mm. bore × 130 mm. stroke) 16-h.p. Cannstatt-Daimler, mounted centrally, with final drive by chains to the rear wheels. The gear-box was also of the

Cannstatt type and gave four speeds forward, corresponding to $1\frac{1}{2}$, 3, 5 and 9 m.p.h. at 750 r.p.m., and reverse. The engine was designed to run on either petrol or heavy oil. The brakes, it was proudly claimed, could bring the machine from top speed to a halt in 8 yards. They worked on the rear wheels in two stages by operation of a hand wheel, first through bands on the hubs and then, by further rotation of the brake wheel, by application of clamps on the tyres of the wheels.

The demonstration of Simms' Motor War Car at the Crystal Palace was well attended by the Press, but no one from the War Office was present, because, it was alleged by Simms, a committee meeting precluded the attendance of the appropriate officers. A contemporary journal suggested that no doubt the alteration of a button die or the design of a 'dustman's cap' for the Guards was the more important matter in hand. However, the lack of interest by the War Office caused Simms and Vickers, Son & Maxim to abandon the further development of this interesting vehicle.

3 Automitrailleuse Charron, Girardot et Voigt, 1902, France.

An exhibit at the Paris motor exhibition in December 1902 which aroused wide interest in the Press because it was one of the earliest armoured cars seen anywhere was this car built by the Société Charron, Girardot et Voigt.

Constructed for the French Ministry of War, it was a 40-h.p. C.G.V. passenger car with a circular tub-shaped armoured body replacing the rear seats. A Hotchkiss machine-gun with an armoured shield was mounted on a pedestal mounting in the centre of this armoured structure so that it had an all-round field of fire. The armour of the circular body and also the machine-gun shield was about 6–7 mm. Access for the machine-gunner was through a door in the rear. No protection at all was provided for the driver and front-seat passenger or any other part of the car.

The 40-h.p. C.G.V. chassis on which this armoured body was built was strongly influenced by Panhard design: both Charron and Girardot had had close connections with Panhard cars before founding the C.G.V. company in 1901. The engine was a four-cylinder type with automatic inlet valves with a four-speed gear-box and with side-chain drive to the rear wheels.

The 1902 automitrailleuse C.G.V. was tested by the French military authorities in 1903. The War Ministry did not order further cars of this type, but showed enough interest to encourage the builders to develop a fully armoured car with a revolving turret.

4 Daimler Panzerwagen, 1904, Austria.

That great pioneer of the motor industry Gottlieb Daimler established a factory at Wiener-Neustadt in Austria in 1899 for the manufacture of cars designed at the parent works in Germany, near Stuttgart.

Paul Daimler (son of Gottlieb) was chief engineer of the Österreichisches Daimler Motoren AG until 1905, and it was under his supervision that the outstanding little Austro-Daimler armoured car was built. This vehicle had a specification including four-wheel drive, an enclosed hull of curved shape and a dome-shaped rotating turret.

The engine was a 35-h.p. Daimler; drive via shafts and differentials at front and rear was to all four wheels. The armour was of only 3-3½ mm. thickness, and this kept the weight down to just under 3 tons, and so contributed to a creditable—in the circumstances—maximum speed of 28 m.p.h. and a reasonably good hill-climbing ability. The fuel tanks gave a radius of action of 155 miles.

Seats for the driver and co-driver could be raised or lowered by about 12 inches, so that when not in action they could look over the top of the armour. The turret as originally built had a port for a single Maxim water-cooled machine-gun; in 1905 this was modified and two slightly smaller openings were put in so that two Maxims could be operated side by side.

The Austro-Daimler armoured car was demonstrated at the German Imperial Army manoeuvres of 1905 and at the Austro-Hungarian Army manoeuvres in the following year. It was not adopted by either country— the automobile era itself was still at too early a stage for an advanced fighting vehicle to have much chance of success —but this car undoubtedly had an influence on later designs.

5 Automitrailleuse Charron, 1904, France.

To the Société Charron, Girardot et Voigt must go the credit for producing

the first armoured car that was in all its essentials the prototype of vehicles of the same basic layout still being built forty years or more later. Following their semi-armoured machine-gun car of 1902, the company worked on the development of a fully armoured vehicle, and two were built in 1904. One of these was tried out in French Army manoeuvres and then sent to Morocco, and the other was bought by the Russian Imperial Government, by whom it was used to help quell the riots in St Petersburg which broke out from January 1905 onwards. An improved but externally almost identical model of this type of car was built between 1906 and 1908, and ten of these were ultimately ordered by the Russian Government. Two cars in transit through Germany for delivery to the Russians were impounded by the customs authorities and used in the German Army manoeuvres of 1909. However, nine cars were delivered to the Russians by the outbreak of war in 1914.

The Charron armoured car (the firm, at Puteaux, Seine, became a British limited company in 1906, when Girardot left the partnership, and adopted the title Automobiles Charron Ltd.) was based on the touring-car chassis with pneumatic tyres and the characteristic underslung radiator, the cooling air flowing through a rectangular box mounted low on the front of the bonnet. The vehicle was completely armoured, and the revolving turret mounted on the hull roof towards the rear carried one Hotchkiss machine-gun. A U-shaped channel projected from the front of the turret to protect the machine-gun barrel—this appears to be the first instance of this device; one which appealed to the Russians because some similar arrangement was used on nearly all their armoured cars in the First World War. For use in action the driver had a small shuttered loophole for vision, with a similar loophole for the co-driver. For other times, however, the car had exceptionally good vision facilities, because the whole plate in front of the driver hinged upwards, and there were also two large apertures each side of the hull. Other features of the Charron car were self-sealing tyres and steel channels (carried over the rear wheels) for use in crossing ditches or other minor obstacles.

The later cars differed from the earlier ones in having 35-h.p. instead of 30-h.p. engines and an increased performance, further helped by a weight reduction from about 3¼ tons to just over 2½ tons. Externally they appear to have been the same, except that mudguards were not used in the later cars.

6 Armstrong-Whitworth Armoured Cars, 1906 and 1913, U.K.

In 1904 production of the Wilson-Pilcher car was undertaken by the famous armament firm of Sir W. G. Armstrong, Whitworth & Co. Ltd. at Newcastle-upon-Tyne. It was therefore quite appropriate that an armoured car should have been built two years later, designed by W. G. Wilson. Unfortunately, few technical details of the chassis are available, but it appears to have had the six-cylinder four-litre engine with a four-speed epicyclic gear-box—the first of its type.

The car had large-diameter, wooden-spoked wheels with solid rubber tyres, which gave it a high ground clearance and good obstacle-crossing capacity. The armour enclosed the body and engine (although in photographs the engine side panels are shown removed, possibly indicating cooling problems) but came little above the driver's waist level and offered no overhead protection at all. The armament, intended to be mounted with a shield at the front to the left of the driver, was a Vickers-Maxim 1-pdr. quick-firing automatic gun—the 'pom-pom'.

An interesting feature of this 1906 vehicle was the drum of light steel cable with which, through power take-off pulleys on either side of the hull, it could pull itself out of difficulties in heavy going.

Although appearing to be somewhat massive, this car was, in fact, only about 12 ft long, 5 ft wide and 5 ft high —much smaller than most of the armoured cars used in the First World War.

The Armstrong-Whitworth firm did not follow up this early effort until 1913, when they were invited to build an experimental armoured car for the Imperial Russian Government. This car was quite small, but fully armoured with a cylindrical revolving turret mounting a Maxim machine-gun. Like the 1906 design, it had spoked wheels with solid rubber tyres (dual at the rear) and a high ground clearance.

The car is shown in the drawing bearing the winged wheels used as a symbol by the Russian motor-transport troops—a badge still in use by the Red Army at least until 1955. The Russians were among the first to realize the potential of armoured cars, and the

Armstrong-Whitworth was one of many to be supplied later by Britain (although not, as it happened, on Armstrong-Whitworth chassis) and other countries right up to the Revolution in 1917.

7 Panzerkraftwagen Ehrhardt (5-cm. BAK), 1906, Germany.

In the early years of the twentieth century the potential value of the dirigible balloon, or airship, for military reconnaissance purposes was recognized in several countries, not least in Germany, the home of Count Zeppelin, and the German firm of Ehrhardt was the first to develop an armoured anti-balloon vehicle.

The Ehrhardt BAK (Ballon Abwehr Kanone), as the vehicle is usually known, appeared in 1906 and was based on a conventional light lorry chassis with a 50/60-h.p. engine with chain drive to the rear wheels and pneumatic tyres. The armoured superstructure was only $3\frac{1}{2}$ mm. thick, and the whole vehicle weighed just over 3 tons and had a speed of 29 m.p.h. The gun, a 5-cm. weapon built by Rheinmetall, was mounted on the roof in a turret placed in approximately the centre of the vehicle. The mounting permitted almost vertical elevation for anti-aircraft use. With depression slightly below horizontal the gun also had some potential against ground targets in the field, but for either purpose the absence of full traverse placed a limit on its usefulness.

8 5·7-cm. Flak auf Daimler Panzerkraftwagen, 1909, Germany.

The Krupp-Daimler armoured anti-aircraft vehicle was an improvement over the Ehrhardt BAK of three years before in two important respects—first, the gun was on a fully rotating mounting and, second, the vehicle itself with four-wheel drive had greater mobility.

The Krupp 5·7-cm. L/30 anti-aircraft gun was mounted on a turntable on the lorry platform over the rear axle and was enclosed in a cylindrical turret with a curved, sloping face. Although cramped, the gun could be served by the crew from inside the turret. The main ammunition supply was, however, in racks in the side of the lorry, with external access only, so the gun could not be operated with the vehicle completely closed down.

The armour protection was $3\frac{1}{2}$ mm., that around the driver's cab being arranged so that the upper part could be folded down to the driver's shoulder height when out of action.

The Daimler lorry chassis was of the type in which the rear axle was carried on a sub-frame. Transmission was by shafts to front and rear axles. The front tyres were solid rubber, the rear ones pneumatic.

A somewhat similar Krupp-Daimler vehicle was built in 1910, but this was unarmoured, because, following the 1909 manoeuvres in which the first Krupp-Daimler BAK and other armoured vehicles took part, it was decided that armoured cars had only limited uses in special situations.

9 Automitrailleuse Hotchkiss, 1909, France.

The first armoured car built by the famous armaments firm of Hotchkiss et Cie, of St Denis, Seine, was completed in 1909 and was generally very similar in layout to the C.G.V. car of seven years earlier. Mechanically, however, it had the advantages of the advances in automobile design that had taken place since the beginning of the century, and featured shaft drive to the rear axle, in the development of which the Hotchkiss company had played a leading part.

The mounting of the Hotchkiss machine-gun and the armour arrangement were much like that of the 1902 C.G.V., although access for the gunner was by means of a door in the armour on the left-hand side. The driver and co-driver were unprotected from enemy or elements, apart from a metal plate attached to the front of the armoured body and extending over their heads.

Four of these Hotchkiss armoured cars were ordered by the Sultan of Turkey and were delivered in 1909. The Young Turk revolution broke out not long afterwards: the cars were taken over by the revolutionaries and were used by them in overthrowing the Sultan's government.

10 **Armoured Ivel Tractor,** c. 1910, U.K.

The three-wheeled tractor, designed by Dan Albone of Biggleswade, Bedfordshire, was the first successful agricultural tractor operating on petrol to be put on the market in Britain. Produced by Ivel Agricultural Motors from 1903 onwards, the little three-wheelers built up a great reputation for reliability and hard work. The Ivel tractor was driven by a two-cylinder engine of around 20 h.p. This was a proprietary make—

either Aster or Payne and Bates. Transmission was via cone-type friction clutches with final drive by a roller chain to a differential on the back axle. There was no variable gearing, the gear change lever offering three positions only—forwards, neutral, and reverse. The driver, as in most modern agricultural tractors, sat at the rear between the large wheels, although in the Ivel his seat was offset to the right with a large water cooling tank beside him on the left.

The Ivel tractor was used as the basis of an early armoured vehicle, which appeared about 1910. The engine and the driver's position were completely enclosed. Access was from the rear via folding armoured doors. The purpose for which this vehicle was intended is not known, although it might have been as an artillery towing machine. The Royal Marines showed some interest in the Ivel, apparently as an armoured ambulance, although this could only have been in conjunction with a trailer. One feature of the Ivel was that it could be remotely controlled (for use with a binder for example) by means of an extension steering wheel and a rope to the gear lever. This apparatus could conceivably have widened the scope of the Ivel as a military vehicle but, as far as can be ascertained, it never went beyond the experimental stage in its warlike guise.

11 **Automitragliatrice Isotta-Fraschini,** 1911, Italy.

The earliest Italian armoured car, the Isotta-Fraschini of 1911, exhibited the layout which during the next thirty-forty years came to be regarded as conventional—front engine, fully enclosed armoured hull surmounted by a rotating turret.

Designed by the talented engineer Guistino Cattaneo (whose efforts by 1909 had resulted, thanks to successes in racing, in 75% of Isotta-Fraschinis being exported, mainly to the United States), the armoured car showed few of the features of its sporting relatives. The bonnet, however, although armoured retained the V-fronted shape of the private cars and carried the Isotta-Fraschini motif. The hull armour was built up of 4-mm. plate and included protection for the rear wheels. Two machine-guns were carried, one in the turret and the other in a mounting in the rear of the hull. Total weight of the car was around 3 tons, and a top speed of about 37 m.p.h. could be attained. The tyres (dual at the rear) were solid rubber, but to help avoid sinkage in sand or other soft ground the front wheels were fitted with steel flanges.

Several of these cars were built and were shipped to North Africa in 1912 for use in the Italo-Turkish war.

12 **Autoblindata Fiat,** 1912, Italy.

The first Fiat armoured car was built in 1912, towards the end of the Italo-Turkish war. During this conflict the open spaces of the Libyan desert pointed out the advantages of motor transport—it was this area in which fierce mechanized battles were to be fought thirty years later, and the Fiat, together with a few other types of armoured cars, was sent to North Africa for experimental use.

Similar in general layout to the slightly earlier Isotta-Fraschini, the

Fiat was less compact, but interesting in that pneumatic tyres were introduced.

Armoured and equipped at the Arsenale di Artigliera in Turin, the main armament was one water-cooled machine-gun in a revolving turret which for night operations carried also a small searchlight.

13 **Camion Protegido Schneider,** 1914, France.

This massive armoured vehicle was manufactured by the French armament firm of Schneider at Le Creuseot. Twenty-four were constructed on 24-40 h.p. chassis and supplied to the Spanish Army for employment in Morocco. They were intended for use as mobile blockhouses and as such were liberally provided with ports for the operation of small arms. (It is rather amusing to note that a picture postcard artist of the First World War happened to choose this vehicle as the basis of a drawing of a typical armoured car in action and imaginatively showed, in addition to small arms poking from the more likely positions, a large calibre cannon projecting from the side and two rifles sticking out of the radiator grilles!)

The hull of the vehicle was protected by 5-mm. armour plate and the interior was divided into three compartments—the front one for the driver and officer in command. The middle section was for the fighting crew and here there were four wide 'letter box' rifle slits on each side, on two levels. The V-shaped roof over both front compartments was hinged and could be opened —no doubt a welcome amenity for the crew in the North African summer. The rear compartment was enclosed and was for ammunition—nearly 3 tons could be carried.

14 Automitrailleuse Minerva, 1914 Belgium.

Belgium was the first country to suffer invasion at the beginning of the First World War but the Belgians were also the first to make extensive use of automobiles to strike back. At first unarmoured touring cars—Excelsiors, Minervas and others—were pressed into service to carry sharpshooters equipped with rifles or machine-guns on lightning raids against the advancing Germans, a form of warfare in which the Belgians—fast and aggressive motorists—were well suited. Nevertheless, the advantage of protection for the crews was quickly realized and temporary armour plates were added only shortly afterwards to some cars. At the same time, a standard pattern of armour was devised and the first Minerva cars fitted with this sort of armour were coming out of the Antwerp factory by the third week of August 1914.

The armour designed for the Minerva —5-mm. plate was used—consisted of a simple open-topped crew compartment with vertical sides and a rounded rear end. There was also separate protection for the radiator with two small doors. Besides Minervas, roughly the same form of armour was applied to other suitable touring car chassis that happened to be available, including Mercedes. Stowage was provided on the mudguards at either side and the spare wheel was carried in a well over the rear axle.

The armament was usually one Hotchkiss machine-gun mounted in the crew compartment—at first without a shield although later one was fitted. Some cars ('Autocanon') carried instead of the machine-gun a 37-mm. cannon.

A modification of the normal type was fully enclosed and had the rear portion of the hull raised in height. This part had observation ports and the car was possibly intended as a command vehicle.

The Minerva chassis used for these armoured cars used Knight pattern sleeve-valve engines and were well-built vehicles of good performance. The only major change to the standard chassis was in the introduction of dual rear wheels to take the extra weight of the armour and equipment. This early type of Minerva armoured car was used throughout the war on the Western Front and some were also with the Belgian armoured car battery which supported the Russians, until withdrawn in 1917. Some 1914 Minervas were still in service in the Belgian Army almost up to the outbreak of the Second World War.

15 Armoured Car, Rolls-Royce (first R.N.A.S. pattern) 1914, U.K.

The possibility of aerial attack on London and south-east England by German airships based on the German coast and, perhaps, Belgium, was feared by Winston Churchill, First Lord of the Admiralty. With characteristic energy, he drafted a series of minutes in September 1914 which first ordered a Royal Naval aeroplane force to be stationed on the French coast to seek out and destroy Zeppelin airship bases and then for a force of 200–300 men with 100 armed motor cars to be raised to give support to the aeroplanes and protect their aerodromes against marauding German cavalry.

The squadron of the Royal Naval Air Service based at Eastchurch, Kent was sent to Dunkirk to perform this task under the command of Commander C. R. Samson, R.N. A resourceful and aggressive officer, Samson quickly instituted motor car patrols, many of which he led himself. The only ground machine-gun available in the squadron was mounted on one car (originally for anti-aircraft use but later modified for horizontal fire also) and two further machine-guns, borrowed from the French, were fitted on other cars on 5 September 1914. Early encounters with Uhlan (German cavalry) patrols were successful but Samson was quick to realize the value of armour protection and permission was obtained from the Admiralty to have armour fitted locally to some of the cars belonging to the squadron.

This work was carried out by the Dunkirk shipyard Forges et Chantiers de France, to designs produced by Lieutenant F. R. Samson, R.N.V.R. (C. R. Samson's brother and a member of the squadron). In order to keep down the weight, the armour was confined to the radiator, in front of the driver, and a V-shaped shield at the rear, swept upwards to increase protection for the machine-gunner—a Maxim being mounted near the rear. This design gave fairly good protection from the front and the rear although the driver, in particular, was rather inadequately guarded at the sides.

The first car to be armoured in this way was a 45–50 h.p. Mercedes tourer —F. R. Samson's own car—and this was followed by a Rolls-Royce 40/50 h.p. This car, shown in the drawings, was a Silver Ghost of the 'Alpine' type, with larger brake drums than the standard model. The armour used for both these cars was only boiler plate, which in tests was found to be proof against English rifle bullets only at 500 yards upwards—the protection it gave was more moral than real—and Commander Samson and his officers requested supplies of real armour plate from England and drew up designs for a proper armoured car.

This first R.N.A.S. pattern of armour was also applied to two or more armoured cars used by the French, apparently Delaunay–Bellevilles. For whom these cars were originally built is uncertain (although it seems a few Delaunay–Belleville chassis may have been sent to the R.N.A.S. in France for experimental purposes), but it is likely that, like the Mercedes and Rolls-Royce, they were constructed by Forges et Chantiers de France. Finally, Samson included an Austro–Daimler 27/80 h.p. chassis described as armoured in a return dated 26 December 1914, and this may also have had the same pattern of armour.

16 Armoured L.G.O.C. 'B' Type chassis (R.N.A.S.), 1914, U.K.

After Commander C. R. Samson's aeroplane and armoured car force had been reinforced by a detachment of 200 Royal Marines on 8 September 1914, it was decided to try and provide support for the machine-gun cars—both armoured and unarmoured—by infantry carried in lorries. So that the infantry could go right in with the machine-gun cars, an armoured lorry was designed by Lieutenant F. R. Samson, assisted by Commander C. R. Samson.

The same basic principles used in the designs for the armour for the 45–50 h.p. Mercedes and 40/50 h.p. Rolls-Royce touring cars were again employed—to cut down extra weight as far as possible, only frontal protection was given to the engine. The driver's position had backward sloping armour and the open body at the rear had inward sloping armour which made the most effective use of the boiler plate which was the only 'armour' available. This, of course, gave protection only at ranges of 500 yards upwards. Twelve Royal Marine riflemen could be carried and loopholes were provided to enable them to use their weapons from the vehicle.

The work on these armoured cars was carried out by Forges et Chantiers de France at Dunkirk. Two vehicles were armoured in this way and ex-L.G.O.C. 'B' type omnibus chassis were used. This sturdy and reliable type of vehicle was well capable of carrying the weight of the armour but it was found that they were too slow to keep up with the machine-gun cars in action. Touring cars with lorry bodies were again used to carry the riflemen on Samson's operations and the two armoured L.G.O.C. 'B' type vehicles seem to have been used only for guard duties.

Two further fighting vehicles using the 'B' type chassis were designed by C. R. Samson and his officers—a 3-pdr. Vickers semi-automatic gun mounted

on the lorry platform and an anti-aircraft gun mounting. The 3-pdr. lorry mounting was delivered by Forges et Chantiers de France on 16 October 1914, and was used in action fairly regularly in the Dunkirk area until the roads became too bad by the third week in November. The lorry carried 96 rounds of 3-pdr. ammunition and a ladder was later acquired and carried for observation purposes.

Another armoured car on a lorry chassis which Samson's squadron designed and had built was a five-ton Mercedes completely armoured and equipped with six machine-guns. Uncommon features for the time—and typical of the thought that went into the designs evolved by the R.N.A.S. in France—were a conning tower for the car commander and an extra steering wheel for driving in reverse in emergency.

17 Armoured Cars, Rolls-Royce (first Admiralty pattern) and Wolseley (first Admiralty pattern), 1914, U.K.

In pursuance of Winston Churchill's instructions to provide armed motor cars to support the Royal Naval Air Service aeroplane force in France, suitable chassis were ordered or requisitioned from British motor manufacturers — principally Rolls-Royce, Wolseley, and Talbot, all of whom had powerful touring car chassis in production in 1914. Following reports from Commander Samson in France, the Admiralty Air Department (which controlled the R.N.A.S.) designed armour to be fitted to a proportion of the cars sent out. Armoured cars of this first Admiralty pattern were received by Samson during September and October 1914.

The armour designed for both Rolls-Royce and Wolseley cars (the 40/50 h.p. Silver Ghost and the 30/40 h.p. six-cylinder models respectively—the only major change to standard specification being the use of twin rear tyres) was on very simple lines and consisted of full protection for the engine, and armour for the sides and back of the rear compartment, which was open. The driver, however, was provided with an armoured head cover, open at the front. This appears to have been intended to give the driver some protection from the noise in action of the machine-gun, which was mounted over his head. In both models remotely controlled armoured radiator doors were fitted—in the Wolseleys a single door opening upwards and in the Rolls-Royces two doors, opening outwards. Some slight frontal protection was given to the tyres by plates attached to the front of the front mudguards.

Cars of this type, and similar Talbots, had been delivered in batches to Samson's force based at Dunkirk in some quantity by the end of September 1914. The total is difficult to ascertain but the armoured car organisation by about early October provided for four squadrons, equipped with 18 Rolls-Royce, 21 Wolseley and 21 Talbot armoured cars.

The Admiralty pattern cars were not very popular with Samson's men, because, apart from the driver, they gave little protection to the crew—the side armour coming only to below waist level for a standing man. They were, nevertheless, used fairly extensively on operations (together with other armoured and unarmoured R.N.A.S. vehicles including, incidentally, 30/40 h.p. Wolseley 'wagons' used for detachments of Royal Marine riflemen) until after the middle of October. By early November trench warfare had set in and the force of Royal Marines manning the cars was sent back to England.

The Wolseley cars were less successful than the others and it is believed that the armour was removed and light wooden lorry bodies fitted so that they could be used as tenders. The Rolls-Royce chassis, on the other hand, were very reliable and stood up to the heavy work well, and this make was used for the majority of the later Admiralty turreted pattern armoured cars. It is believed that the cars with the early types of armour were stripped down and rebuilt, although before this one Rolls-Royce first Admiralty pattern, at least, was modified to a design by Commander C. R. Samson in conjunction with his brother, Lieutenant F. R. Samson, R.N.V.R., and Lieutenant T. Warner, R.M.L.I., the squadron armament officer. In this car, the original armour was left intact, but the driver's head cover was removed and the whole crew compartment was completely enclosed with pyramid-shaped armour with a flat roof, on top of which was mounted a Lewis-machine-gun. This vehicle was used as the tractor for a 3-pdr. naval gun with a shield on a carriage fitted with Rudge Whitworth dual wire-spoked wheels. The gun mounting was also designed by the R.N.A.S. squadron officers, and others of this type were built and used later in France, Gallipoli, and with the Russian expedition.

18 **Armoured Cars, Talbot (first Admiralty pattern and modified first Admiralty pattern),** 1914, U.K.

Together with Rolls-Royces and Wolseleys, chassis supplied by Clement–Talbot Ltd., of North Kensington, London, were used for the first pattern of armoured car designed by the Admiralty Air Department in September 1914. The Clement–Talbot Company was originally formed to import French Clément cars into the United Kingdom, but the 25/50 h.p. chassis of 1914 used for the armoured cars was entirely British designed and built. The standard touring car chassis with a four-cylinder engine of 101·5 mm. bore and 140 mm. stroke with four-speed gear-box was used, the only important change being the substitution of artillery-type wheels with Warland dual rims and twin rear tyres for the usual Talbot detachable wheels.

The armour designed for these cars was very similar to that of the Wolseleys and Rolls-Royces, with the main difference that the Talbots, as delivered from the factory, had a large rectangular armour plate in front of the radiator. This projected above the top line of the engine bonnet and although it also offered some slight frontal protection to the driver, it at the same time obscured a good deal of his view of the road. However, some Talbot armoured cars in use in France and Belgium had, instead, twin sideways-opening armoured radiator doors—a much better design—as well as fully protected front wheels and it seems at least possible that these cars were some of those armoured in France with the supply of Beard-more armour plate sent out about October 1914 by the Admiralty to Samson's R.N.A.S. squadron from England.

Some of the Talbots were used without the driver's head cover and radiator protection plate and seem to have been employed only to carry supplies. This may have only been pending conversion, however, because by the beginning of November a modified Admiralty-pattern Talbot armoured car was on the road in France. In this type the original armour was, in the main, left unaltered except that the rear wheel covers and the driver's head cover were removed. The armour over the crew compartment was built up to the shoulder height of a member of the crew standing up. It sloped inwards, but the roof was left open. The armament carried was either two Maxim machine-guns or one Maxim with a shield.

Six Talbots of this completely new type were built by Forges et Chantiers de France at Dunkirk under the supervision of Lieutenant F. R. Samson who had helped to design them. These modified Admiralty pattern cars amounted, in effect, to the second R.N.A.S. pattern and incorporated the results of the experience gained by the armoured car crews in action. The modified Talbots were given names commemorating actions in which Samson's armoured cars had been engaged, such as Cassel, Orchies, Aniche and Douai. They were delivered by the first week of November 1914, when the opportunities for their employment had almost gone, although a section of the newly armoured cars was sent to the La Bassée area to be tried out.

19 Autocar Armoured Car, 1914, U.S.A.

The first contingent of the Canadian Army expeditionary force arrived in England on 16 October 1914, equipped with a 'motor machine-gun corps' of twenty armoured cars. This formation —the first in the First World War designed and equipped right from the start as an armoured force—was the outcome of the enterprise shown by Raymond Brutinel. Brutinel had served in the French Army and became convinced of the value of the machine-gun. Living in Canada at the outbreak of war in 1914, he persuaded wealthy business contemporaries led by Sir Clifford Sifton to join with him in raising and equipping a brigade of motor machine-guns.

The cars were ordered from the Autocar Company, of Ardmore, Pennsylvania, U.S.A. They were standard commercial chassis with solid tyres armoured with $\frac{3}{4}$-in. ($9\frac{1}{2}$-mm.) plate supplied by the Bethlehem Steel Corporation. The armour gave all-round protection but was unusual in that it not only offered no head cover for the driver, but had no vision port in the front plate. However, the cars were not intended to go into action as fighting vehicles but to act as carriers for the two machine-guns normally provided in each car. These machine-guns were originally air-cooled, American-made Colts but later, with the Canadian Corps in France, 0·303-in. Vickers water-cooled machine-guns were used instead.

King George V, when inspecting the 1st Canadian Motor Machine-Gun Brigade at Aldershot shortly after their arrival from Canada, expressed the opinion that the unit should prove very useful—a view that did not coincide with general military opinion at the time. The Canadian motor machine-guns were, however, of great value in France, from their arrival in 1915 to the end of the war—perhaps at their best in holding the German offensive of March 1918—in providing a mobile reserve of fire power.

20 Automitrailleuse S.A.V.A., 1914 Belgium.

Some of the first enclosed versions of Belgian armoured cars were built by about October 1914, including the S.A.V.A. with turret shown in the drawings. This step was said to have been brought about by public opinion in Belgium after the distinguished crew of an open top armoured car, headed by Prince Baudouin de Ligne, had all been killed during a raiding expedition to destroy a bridge behind the German lines. The improvement of enclosing the car and adding a turret was, in any event, a logical one and the same line of development was followed also in the British and French armoured cars of the same period.

The chassis was provided by the Société Anversoise pour Fabrication de Voitures Automobiles (S.A.V.A.) of Antwerp—a firm which was founded in 1910 and was bought up by Minerva in 1923. It was a powerful sporting vehicle, suited to carry the weight of the armour which was constructed by the Cockerill firm of Seraing, near Liege.

The engine as well as the crew compartment was fully enclosed. The frontal protection was enhanced by the armour in front of the driver being a curved plate, sloping up from the engine bonnet to merge with the roof line. The turret ring followed the curve of the rear of the hull and the turret itself was dome-shaped and open at the rear. It was equipped with one Hotchkiss air-cooled machine-gun. Small side doors in the hull beneath the turret were provided to give access to the interior of the car. The equipment included a large spotlight on the left-hand side of the bonnet in addition to the usual head-lamps.

There was also an enclosed version of the Minerva with a half-dome turret and armoured in a generally similar way to the S.A.V.A.

21 **Autocanon 37-mm. Renault,** 1914, France.

The great Renault concern at Billancourt, near Paris, which was responsible for about one-fifth of all passenger cars built in France in 1914 was obviously an important unit in the French war effort. Among its earliest war productions was a preliminary order for 100 armoured cars. The earliest of these had improvised armour—'blindage de fortune'—built on the 18-h.p. Renault and other chassis without major modifications. By November 1914, however, a standard pattern was being delivered in which dual rear wheels were introduced. A truck-type armoured body was fitted mounting a machine-gun on a pivot and protected in some cars, but not all, by a large flat shield. The engine armour disguised the famous Renault dashboard radiator:

there was an air intake at the front of the bonnet.

Louis Renault was infuriated by being told, after the first 100 armoured cars had been completed—with difficulty because of a shortage of armour plate—to convert them to ambulances! Renault refused and it appears that the decision was altered and the conversions were not carried out.

Late in 1914 appeared the Renault which, in both Automitrailleuse and Autocanon forms, continued in use throughout the war. This car was recognizably a Renault because the front portion of the bonnet was made as low as possible and the armoured grilles of the dashboard radiator appeared behind it at the front of the crew compartment. The hull was open topped and the armament—either an air-cooled machine-gun or a 37-mm. gun—was mounted here. A gun shield was fitted in either case, although that for the machine-gun was rather more V-shaped.

The chassis with the 18-h.p. four-cylinder 95/160 engine was again used. This had semi-elliptic springs and detachable wooden-spoked, pneumatic-tyred wheels, dual at the rear.

France ended the war with only 39 Renault armoured cars left, so losses must have been heavy although it must also be said that armoured car production from the end of 1915 onwards was concentrated on White imported chassis.

22 **Isotta-Fraschini Armoured Car (built for Russia)**, 1914, U.K.

Charles Jarrott, the famous racing driver, was invited by the Imperial

Russian Government in 1914 to design and supply a prototype armoured car. Jarrott chose as the basis for his design the imported Italian Isotta-Fraschini 100–120-h.p. chassis. The layout of his vehicle appears to have been inspired by the Isotta-Fraschini armoured car built in Italy in 1911 and the finished product was, in fact, very like its forerunner in external appearance in many respects.

The armour protection was comprehensive, enclosing engine, hull, and the back wheels although the front wheels were not provided even with mudguards. The hull armour was built up on a wooden frame, to which the plates were attached. On the hull roof was mounted a multi-sided turret with provision for one machine-gun. Oddly enough, although the car had seating accommodation for no less than nine men, the only other weapon position, apart from the turret, was in the rear doors, where a second machine-gun could be mounted.

Unfortunately, no performance figures are available for this armoured car. Its massive four-cylinder engine of nearly 11,000 c.c. must have given it a quite respectable speed on good roads however, although its weight and solid rubber tyres probably limited severely the car's usefulness in Russia outside the main towns.

The Isotta-Fraschini armoured car appears to have been ordered about September or October 1914: it was completed by the beginning of November by Jarrott's firm, Charles Jarrott & Letts Ltd., passed and accepted by Russian officers in London and shipped to Archangel in the same month.

23 Armoured Car, Rolls-Royce (Admiralty turreted pattern), 1914, U.K.

For many people, the name Rolls-Royce still conjures up the idea of 'armoured car', at least as much as visions of the urbane life associated with what is claimed to be 'the Best Car in the World'. The reason is easy to find because not only did Rolls-Royce armoured cars serve on many fronts as far apart as South-West Africa and Russia from 1914 onwards in the First World War, but in a recognizably similar form were employed in the British and other armies throughout the inter-war years all over the world, and again in action during the earlier years of the Second World War.

The foundation of this story of successful longevity really lies in the London–Edinburgh trials of the year 1911 when Rolls-Royce cars established their reputation for high quality combined with strength and reliability. After the outbreak of war, early reports from Commander C. R. Samson's R.N.A.S. aeroplane and armoured car force at Dunkirk confirmed that mechanically the best of his improvised armoured cars were undoubtedly the Rolls-Royces.

In September 1914, all Rolls-Royce chassis in the works at Derby, or in the hands of coachbuilders or agents, and some cars completed with coachwork were requisitioned. These were all of the 'Silver Ghost' model which had been standardized since 1908. The engine was a six-cylinder 7428-c.c. unit described as 40/50 h.p. and developing a maximum of around 80 b.h.p. The gear-box was a four-speed type in 1914 cars although it is believed that a few earlier cars with the three-speed gearbox may also have been among those converted to armoured cars.

Design of the turreted pattern Rolls-Royce armoured car was commenced about October 1914, following discussions as to how to provide better protection than that offered by the early open top armoured vehicles. A small committee was formed in the Admiralty Air Department to consider this problem. Leading members were Squadron Commander W. Briggs and Flight Commander T. G. Hetherington (both of the R.N.A.S.) and they were assisted by Lord Wimborne and Mr N. C. Macnamara. A rough design of car with a turret was worked out and a model was made in three-ply wood. This involved some curved armour plates and Mr Scott of William Beardmore and Co. evolved a method of bending light armour plate.

After the design was finalized, production went ahead and the first three Rolls-Royce armoured cars of the turreted pattern were delivered on 3 December 1914. The complement for the first R.N.A.S. squadron of the Armoured Car Division—twelve armoured cars—was completed during December and the squadron was sent to the East Coast of England both for trials and to guard against invasion. In service, heavier suspension was found to be necessary and new springs, consisting of thirteen leaves at the front and fifteen leaves at the rear, were fitted on these cars and standardized for all later Rolls-Royce armoured cars. The new axle casings were also changed for a heavier pattern.

A total of six squadrons of Rolls-Royce armoured cars was completed by the end of January 1915 but Maxim machine-guns had to be obtained from ships of the Fleet fully to equip them all.

Training went ahead quickly, and in March the first two squadrons were sent on active service overseas—one to France (and later to Egypt) and the other to German South-West Africa from whence in July a section went on to East Africa. Early experience in action in France suggested the need for a plate on the gun barrel to protect the open mounting and this was fitted on many cars later. In Africa the cars won praise for their mechanical reliability (although conditions in some areas precluded the use of the higher gears for days on end), but the twin Rudge Whitworth rear wheels filled with Rubberine (a puncture sealing substance) were often in urgent need of replacement.

In April two further squadrons were sent to Gallipoli where, however, only one major opportunity presented itself for armoured car action.

From August 1915 onwards the Royal Naval Air Service Armoured Car Division was broken up and most of the equipment was handed over to the Army. Some Rolls-Royce armoured cars were at this time stripped of their armour and converted into ambulances, light lorries or tenders. Others remained in service in Light Armoured Motor Batteries of the Army, including the cars in Egypt and Palestine and the ones that took part in Colonel T. E. Lawrence's campaign.

Two Rolls-Royce armoured cars were in Russia with Commander Locker-Lampson's force (which remained a Royal Naval Air Service detachment) until the Revolution in 1917—

one of these was claimed to have done 53,000 miles over terrible roads or no roads at all with only minor repairs.

The Rolls-Royce 1914 Admiralty turreted pattern armoured car needs little description: its basic layout with a central driver's and fighting compartment topped by a revolving turret and and open platform behind was used for other types of British armoured cars right up to the Second World War. The crew was normally three men—the driver sitting on the floor on a cushion and, in action, the other two standing to serve the Vickers machine-gun mounted in the turret. Space was limited inside the car, however, and for this reason sometimes the crew was only two, in which case the driver fed the machine-gun, when driving, with one hand.

There were a few modifications and variants of the basic type. One experimental car had the turret removed and a 1-pdr. automatic gun ('pom pom') fitted on an open mounting. Some cars used in Egypt and Arabia had either the top plates of the turret or the turret itself removed to make the interior more bearable in the hot climate. For engaging and pulling away barbed wire entanglements, some cars in France had a pivoted hook fitted at the front—this idea apparently originated at Gallipoli, where Turkish trenches were attacked in this way. To protect the car commanders a small square armoured cupola was added on the turrets of some Rolls-Royce armoured cars.

Some Rolls-Royce armoured cars of this 1914 pattern (together with cars of the very similar 1920 pattern) remained in service for many years after the War

—notably with the Royal Tank Corps in India and with the Royal Air Force Armoured Car Companies in Iraq. Some of the R.A.F. cars (somewhat modernized) were still in active use at Habbaniya as late as 1941.

24 Packard Armoured Car, 1914, U.S.A.

The second Canadian contingent for overseas service was equipped, like the first contingent, with American armoured cars. Unlike the Autocars of the first contingent, these were built on passenger car chassis—six-cylinder 38-h.p. Packards, with wire-spoke wheels and pneumatic tyres. They were ordered by the Canadian Government through the Ontario Motor Car Co., Toronto, from the Packard Motor Car Company of Detroit, Michigan.

The body of these cars was fully enclosed by armour. The driver had a vision port the full width of the car and there was also an opening flap in the roof over his head. Unusual triangular loop holes were provided in the hull sides. The engine was also fully protected: the armoured radiator door could be opened or closed from the driver's position. A cylindrical turret was mounted on the hull roof on ball bearings and was equipped with one Colt air-cooled machine-gun. The gunner sat on a bicycle saddle.

A contemporary account of the mobilization of the second Canadian contingent in December 1914, refers to three armoured cars and mentions an order for eight more from the Packard Motor Car Company but, unfortunately, nothing further is known of any of these armoured cars.

25 **Armoured Cars, Isotta-Fraschini (Westmorland and Cumberland Yeomanry),** 1914 and 1915, U.K.

The Westmorland and Cumberland Yeomanry was a Territorial Army cavalry unit with officers who, more than most of their kind in 1914, were conscious of the benefits that might be obtained from motor vehicles in conjunction with the cavalry. This spirit showed itself in two armoured cars and a wireless van which were designed and paid for out of their own funds by officers of the regiment.

The wireless van, which was completed and fitted out about the end of 1914 was on a 20–25-h.p. Vulcan chassis. The two armoured cars were on Isotta–Fraschini passenger car chassis imported from Milan (Italy) by Guy Lewin Ltd. This London firm also undertook the manufacture of these armoured cars.

The first of the two armoured cars, which was completed by the end of November 1914, was built to the instructions of Mr Christopher Lowther, an officer in the regiment. The chassis was the 25-h.p. Isotta-Fraschini model. The hull was enclosed, although the engine was protected only by armoured radiator doors, adjustable from the driver's seat. The best features of the design were that the hull sides were high enough to offer adequate protection—a failing in many armoured cars which had already seen action in France and Belgium—and that the driver's front plate was effectively sloped to increase its effectiveness. One of Guy Lewin's mechanics who helped build the armoured car felt it advisable to enlist in the Army in order to ensure that it received proper maintenance after it was delivered, and he was duly appointed driver of the car as a private in the Westmorland and Cumberland Yeomanry!

The second armoured car, which was also built at the end of 1914 but appeared in public apparently for the first time in early 1915 (and is called here, for convenient distinction, the 1915 model), was designed by Lieutenant-Colonel Sir Bryan Leighton. Of unusual design, the shape of hull suggests the rhomboidal side elevation of the first British tanks which appeared about a year later. The long sloping front glacis plate and the sharply undercut rear plate of the hull were conscious efforts to improve the efficacy of the armour protection. Access to the engine was difficult—a problem of many armoured vehicles ever since—and doors in the side armour were provided to help overcome this. The car had an armoured roof, but no turret: 'letter box' weapon slits were provided in the hull sides.

Research has not shown whether these two armoured cars accompanied the Westmorland and Cumberland Yeomanry when it went to France in 1915. It seems unlikely, however, because the regiment was split up into divisional cavalry squadrons for infantry divisions and in 1917 was absorbed into the 7th Battalion The Border Regiment—an infantry battalion.

26 **Armoured Car, Lanchester (Admiralty pattern),** 1915, U.K.

The Lanchester car of 1914 was a well-designed, beautifully running, but in many ways unconventional vehicle.

Based on the designs—fully supported by test research—of the great Dr F. W. Lanchester, the cars bearing his name were eminently suitable for conversion to armoured cars and, in fact, Lanchesters were the only cars, beside the Rolls-Royce, of the turreted pattern to be built in quantity for the Royal Naval Air Service Armoured Car Division.

Several 25-h.p. and 38-h.p. Lanchester touring cars were based at Dunkirk with Commander C. R. Samson's force by December 1914 and also one 38-h.p. Lanchester armoured car. Unfortunately, this vehicle has not been identified—it may have been one of the early open top improvised types—but it is likely that all the Lanchesters stood out well in comparison with most of the other touring cars and light lorries in the varied collection of vehicles held by the R.N.A.S. at Dunkirk.

Certain it is, however, that a prototype turreted pattern Lanchester armoured car was built by the early part of December 1914. This car closely foreshadowed in appearance the vehicles which were to go into service later, except that it lacked mudguards and equipment such as unditching boards and did not have electric lighting.

The principal, and, indeed, the only, major change made between the prototype—which was built on a standard 38-h.p. chassis—and the first car of the production series which appeared about January or February 1915 was in the suspension. Rudge Whitworth twin wheels were fitted at the rear instead of singles. These were detachable wire-spoke wheels with wide rims which carried two tyres as opposed to the normal singles which were still fitted at the front. The Lanchester cantilever

rear springs—semi-elliptic leaf type—were duplicated and the front cantilever suspension was reinforced by shock absorbers—coil springs in vertical tubes, the tops of which were attached to the upper part of the main body frame structure. The Lanchester suspension had the great merit of being very much easier on tyre wear than that of the Rolls-Royce armoured cars.

The mechanical layout of the Lanchester, with the engine beside the driver's feet, made possible a more sloping and better protected bonnet in the armoured car than was practicable with more conventional cars. The low centre of gravity also made them very stable. The turret and fighting compartment of the Lanchester were almost identical to the turreted Rolls-Royce, as were the rear platform and stowage boxes (although the latter do not appear to have been fitted to some of the earliest Lanchesters).

Apart from the modifications mentioned, the 38-h.p. chassis used for the Lanchester armoured cars was standard. The six-cylinder, 4·8-litre engine (R.A.C. rating 39 h.p.) developed 65 b.h.p. at 2200 r.p.m.; the gear-box was a three-speed epicyclic type and transmission was by worm drive to the rear axle. As an armoured car weighing between four and five tons the top speed was about 50 m.p.h. The crew consisted of three or four men and the armament was one Vickers-Maxim machine-gun mounted in the turret, although a Lewis light machine-gun was usually also carried, stowed inside the car.

Thirty-six Lanchester armoured cars were completed by the end of March 1915 and were used to equip three squadrons of the R.N.A.S. All of these squadrons were in France by May and one of them later served with the Belgian Army.

Later in 1915, twenty Lanchester armoured cars—apparently the greater part of the equipment of two squadrons which, because of the trench warfare situation, were by then inactive—were sent to the Russians. It was proposed that these cars should later be taken over by the Russian expeditionary force under the command of Commander Oliver Locker-Lampson. This force had as its nucleus both in personnel and equipment the Lanchester squadron which had been supporting the Belgian Army and was supplemented by a heavy squadron of the R.N.A.S. and extra transport, many of the service vehicles being on Lanchester chassis.

The expeditionary force disembarked at Alexandrovsk (near the North Cape) in January 1916. After an immediate set-back, when the cars had to be sent back to the United Kingdom for repair to damage caused by frost and a storm *en route*, the armoured car force operated in support of the Russians through 1916 and 1917 until the Revolution. From the Arctic Circle, the force was sent down to the Caucasus in June 1916, from where detachments pushed down into Turkey and into Persia. Withdrawn from this area, the R.N.A.S. force was sent via the north shore of the Black Sea to support the Russians in Roumania and in Galicia (south Poland) where they were in action before the end of the year. They continued to bolster the Russian armies until the outbreak of the Revolution in November 1917 made further support of no avail.

The twenty Lanchester armoured cars (referred to above) sent to the Russians in 1915 do not appear to have been made available to the R.N.A.S. force when it was in Russia. Some or all of these cars differed from the others in that they lacked the lockers over the rear wheels and had a small square cupola added on top of the turret.

A few other Lanchester armoured cars beyond the original thirty-six appear to have been built, although the details are uncertain. In December 1916 however, the Lanchester Motor Company was asked to give a quotation for supplying a complete set of armour for one of the armoured cars damaged in the fighting in Roumania. The quotation given (for £198—delivery by the end of January 1917) had to be based on Beardmore 8-mm. plate for vertical surfaces because the original slightly thicker type was no longer available.

The Lanchester armoured cars stood up magnificently to the terrific wear and tear imposed by the appalling roads —or absence of them—in the Russian campaign and gave very little mechanical trouble. Some of these cars must almost without doubt have covered more ground on active service than any other fighting vehicles of the First World War.

27 Autocanon Mors, 1915, Belgium

The Société Nouvelles des Automobiles Mors was a French company established in Paris in 1895 which, by 1914, offered a range of cars most of them having imported Belgian Minerva sleeve-valve engines.

The Mors was, therefore, a suitable chassis for Belgian armoured cars to supplement the production of the Minerva factory at Antwerp which was, in any case, surrendered to the Germans when Antwerp fell on 10 October 1914. Mors cars were fitted with improvised armour in August 1914 and used with Minervas and others by the Belgians to resist the German advance. By early 1915 a fully armoured version had appeared.

The Autocanon Mors of 1915 was rather better protected than the Minervas and although without a turret, the large three-sided shield for the 37-mm. cannon gave almost as much protection as the open-backed dome turret of the later Minerva armoured cars. The 5-mm. plate armour which enclosed the hull was quite tall and offered protection to the crew standing up. The roof was enclosed only over the driver's head the remainder being open. No access doors were fitted—the only means of entry being through the top. The mounting for the 37-mm. cannon was pivoted near the rear of the open compartment and the shield attached to it gave the impression from some angles of a rather tall angular turret. An interesting feature of the cannon was the provision for mounting a Hotchkiss machine-gun above it—one of the earliest examples of a coaxial mount of two different types of weapon.

The engine compartment was armoured only at the sides and the front. The cooling through the armour was by means of six square holes in the armour in front of the radiator, covered by six small spaced armour plates. Above and below these, forward sloping shields helped to deflect air through the apertures.

The chassis used for these cars was the

20-h.p. model with a Minerva-built Knight type of sleeve-valve engine, 100-mm. bore and 140-mm. stroke. The main modifications for armoured car use were that the wheels (with 880 × 120-mm. tyres) were dual instead of single at the rear, and a duplicate set of clutch and brake pedals was provided for the use of the co-driver in emergency.

In 1915 a self-contained unit 'Corps des Autos–Canons–Mitrailleuses Russie' was formed for service in Russia. Mors armoured cars formed the main strength of this unit, the others being 18-h.p. Peugeots which were somewhat similar but lacked any form of protection for the engine and also a shield for the 37-mm. gun. To help the supply problem the Peugeots had the same size wheels as the Mors.

The fighting portion of this unit consisted of a battery of two sections, each of five armoured cars, Mors and Peugeot. In addition, the battery commander and the two section commanders each had an armoured command car. These vehicles were also Mors and built on the same chassis as the Autocanons but the hull was rather higher and was divided internally into three compartments. The driver and co-driver were at the front and behind them was a small compartment for the unit commander and another man and containing a map table and navigation equipment. This compartment had a multi-sided observation cupola on the roof, equipped with a periscope. The rear portion of the body of the command cars was of wooden construction and unarmoured and could be used to carry four men or equipment.

The Belgian armoured car unit per-

130

formed good work in the two years it was on the Eastern Front, being several times congratulated for its activities by the Tsar. It was finally recalled in August 1917 when it appeared unlikely to be able to perform further useful service.

28 Armoured Car, Seabrook, 1915, U.K.

Following their successes with machine-gun-armed cars, Commander C. R. Samson and some of his officers of the Eastchurch Squadron R.N.A.S. designed a lorry-mounted 3-pdr. Vickers semi-automatic gun and had this built, like some of the squadrons' earlier designs, by Forges et Chantiers de France at Dunkirk. The lorry was delivered on 16 October 1914 and was first taken into action in support of the 2nd Life Guards (3rd Cavalry Division) the next day. Many subsequent occasions were found for successful use of this car, even after the machine-gun cars had been taken out of action because of the changed situation brought about by trench warfare and the onset of winter weather, right up to the time that Samson's aeroplane and armoured car force was withdrawn from France.

This performance led to the decision to attach a 3-pdr.-equipped heavy armoured car to each section of the R.N.A.S. armoured car squadrons, which were formed during the winter of 1914/1915. The chassis chosen was the Seabrook 5-ton lorry—an imported American vehicle built by the Standard Motor Truck Co. of Detroit with a four-cylinder Continental 32·2-h.p.engine with chain drive transmission to the rear wheels. The armour

of these cars was rather like a scaled up version of that used for the first Admiralty pattern Wolseleys. The 3-pdr. gun was mounted on a turntable just forward of the rear axle. It had all-round traverse and the armoured sides of the body could be let down to form a platform for the gun crew. The hull armour was built up of 8-mm. plate; some cars, but not all, had a gun shield Four mountings for Vickers-Maxim machine-guns were provided at the corners of the open compartment.

The first Seabrook heavy armoured car was delivered by the Portholme Aerodrome Ltd., Huntingdon, on 5 February 1915. The cars were distributed to the R.N.A.S. Armoured Car squadrons in France and England, three per squadron. It was intended that they should give support to the Rolls-Royce or Lanchester armoured cars in action, although it was before long realized that the much lower speed and manoeuvrability of the Seabrooks made this, in most cases, impracticable.

Samson's 3-pdr. lorry had given no trouble but the armoured Seabrook was a much heavier vehicle of some ten tons loaded weight and the springs, the wheels with their solid rubber tyres, and back axles often gave way. The weight of the cars made it necessary to use the specially carried planks for crossing even small gulleys and this limited their mobility. The gun was able to do useful work, however, and the Commander-in-Chief of the British Expeditionary Force, Sir John French, was sufficiently impressed with their performance around Ypres to ask the Admiralty to send more of them to France. Because of the difficulty of the Seabrooks working with the light armoured cars, and perhaps through Sir John French's request, instructions were given in May 1915 for the heavy armoured cars to be formed into separate squadrons of six cars each. Five such squadrons were formed, most of which served in France. Cars of one squadron were, however, sent to Egypt in November 1915 where they joined the Western Frontier Force in operations against the Senussi. They were insufficiently mobile for desert warfare though, and bogged down in the sand, and in February 1916 were replaced by a Light Armoured Motor Brigade of Rolls-Royce armoured cars.

29 Armoured Car, A.E.C. 'B' Type (War Office pattern), 1915, U.K.

The Associated Equipment Company Ltd. was formed in 1912 to build motor omnibuses for the London General Omnibus Company. A standard model was evolved at the Walthamstow (London) factory which became known as the 'B' type and by 1913 2500 of these buses had been built. Many were taken over by the War Office and used as troop carriers or fitted with lorry bodies —around 1600 in all served with the British Army.

It was an A.E.C. 'B' type chassis that the War Office used for its first experimental armoured car in 1915— the Royal Naval Air Service having armoured a similar type of chassis several months earlier. The 'B' type chassis was somewhat old fashioned in design, a timber frame reinforced by flitch plates. The suspension consisted of semi-elliptic leaf springs. The engine was a four-cylinder T-head side-valve

type which developed about 35 h.p. at 1000 r.p.m.—transmission was by shaft to the rear axle. The four-speed gearbox was one of the best features of the vehicle—it was quiet running and (an even greater virtue) was almost foolproof.

The armoured body designed and built at Woolwich Arsenal for the 'B' type chassis was basically a troop carrier —it had a total of ten ports for the employment of machine-guns or small arms but no provision for a turret or permanently mounted weapons. The armour was vertical or nearly so on all sides with the exception of the driver's position which had a sloped plate. Beside the driver was a somewhat unusual crew position with a sliding shutter for a machine-gun. The driver's cab was fully enclosed (including the back) but the rear body of the vehicle had an open top.

Early in 1915, the Admiralty Air Department was invited to send one of their armoured car experts to the War Office. Flight Commander T. G. Hetherington, who had taken part in experiments on armour protection for the Royal Naval Air Service armoured cars, was then cross-examined by Lord Kitchener and instructed to go to Woolwich Arsenal and inspect and report on this heavy armoured car. Hetherington discovered to his astonishment that the armour was proof only against the German bullet at a range of 100 yards upwards, whereas the R.N.A.S. experiments had led to the use for the Naval armoured cars of Beardmore plate which gave protection against the same bullet at point-blank range. Also, of course, the R.N.A.S. had found out that the armoured car built by Commander

C. R. Samson on a similar chassis was unable to keep up with the machine-gun cars which were the main fighting vehicles and which it was intended to support. The subsequent report by the Admiralty no doubt inhibited the development of the A.E.C. 'B' type armoured car although there is no evidence to suggest that the War Office had pursued this or similar projects with great energy. The R.N.A.S. showed the value of armoured cars on several fronts during 1915, but since the Army absorbed the R.N.A.S. Armoured Car Division (19 squadrons of light and heavy armoured cars and motor-cycle machine-guns) in September of that year there was no further incentive for the War Office to consider the production of armoured cars in any quantity. When further need arose two years later, Austin armoured cars of the type built for Russia were used.

There is some reason to believe that more than one armoured car of this pattern was built—the only employment was for defence of the south and east coasts of England.

30 **Armoured Car, Delaunay-Belleville (Admiralty pattern), and Armoured Car, Talbot (Admiralty turreted pattern)**, 1915, U.K.

It was quite natural that the 25/50-h.p. Talbot chassis, which had already been used for various early Royal Naval Air Service armoured cars in October–November 1914, should be used experimentally when the Admiralty turreted pattern armoured cars were being designed in December. An armoured body and turret very much

like that of the Rolls-Royce was fitted to a Talbot, only the Warland artillery type wheels and the slightly different radiator armour being obviously distinctive features. The Rolls-Royce and Lanchester turreted armoured cars were the most satisfactory vehicles of their kind and the Talbot model was not produced in numbers. In fact, only three of these turreted Talbot armoured cars were built and they went to equip part of one section (establishment of four cars) of one squadron of the R.N.A.S. Armoured Car Division.

The French Delaunay-Belleville had the enviable reputation before the First World War of being one of the best cars available anywhere. Foremost among the owners of Delaunay-Bellevilles was the Tsar of Russia, who possessed a small fleet of them. Delaunay-Bellevilles had been imported into England from France in quite respectable numbers by 1914 and some were assembled in a factory at Maida Vale (North London). This, then was a suitable chassis for adaptation as an armoured car and an armoured hull and turret for the six-cylinder, 35-h.p. 1914 model were designed by the R.N.A.S. Armoured Car Division. The chassis with its cylindrical radiator and bonnet (harking back to the Delaunay-Belleville firm's boiler-making origins) did not lend itself to the pattern of armoured hull used for the Rolls-Royce and a somewhat different type was designed—rather better, in fact, because the sloping driver's plate offered greater protection. The turret too, was different from the usual Admiralty pattern in that it was a simple cylinder without the bevelled edges. The armament, like the other Admiralty turreted armoured cars, consisted of one Vickers-Maxim water-cooled machine-gun.

Only three turreted Delaunay-Belleville armoured cars were built and these helped partly to equip the same R.N.A.S. squadron that had the turreted Talbots. One Delaunay-Belleville, at least, was stripped of its armour not long afterwards and converted into a light lorry used later by the R.N.A.S. Anti-Aircraft Mobile Brigade and an armoured hull from a Delaunay-Belleville armoured car was used on a Killen-Strait tractor chassis in early landship experiments in July 1915.

31 **Garford Armoured Car,** 1915 Russia.

This massive vehicle with upper works suggesting a mediaeval fortress is believed to have been built in the Putilov armament works at Petrograd (now Leningrad) in 1915. The chassis was an imported American 35-h.p. Garford, chain driven on the rear wheels.

The armament was carried in one turret and two sponsons. The turret, facing to the rear with traverse of less than 180 degrees, mounted a short 75-mm. gun with the barrel protected by a curious channel projecting from the turret face, and to the right of it, a Maxim water-cooled machine-gun. In front of the turret and behind the driver's cab were two sponsons, one either side, each with a Maxim machine-gun mounted with an arc of fire sideways and, although limited by the cab, forwards.

The armour ranged between 7 mm. and 9 mm.; the dimensions of the vehicle were about 19 ft long, 7 ft 6 in. wide and 9 ft high. All this added up to

a weight of about 11 tons, which is likely to have severely limited the Garford's mobility in Russian conditions. One did go down in history however, as being the first Russian armoured car to be seen in Teheran, Persia, in 1915.

32 **Armoured, Car, Pierce-Arrow (Anti-Aircraft)** 1915, U.K.

An Anti-Aircraft Brigade was formed by the Royal Marine Artillery in the Autumn of 1914 for service in the field. The equipment chosen for this unit consisted of the Vickers Naval 2-pdr. automatic gun—usually known as 'pom pom'—mounted on Pierce-Arrow 5-ton lorry chassis, armoured.

The establishment fixed for the R.M.A. A.A. Brigade was four batteries, each with four guns, together with supporting transport and a headquarters. Also included were twenty-four motor-cycle combinations equipped with Maxim machine-guns. To ensure that the Brigade was highly mobile, transport was on a generous scale, with thirty-four Pierce-Arrow lorries and two Pierce-Arrow workshop vehicles. Although there were only to be sixteen guns, forty-eight chassis were ordered for them, the balance to be maintained as spares.

The order for the armoured cars (also the Pierce-Arrow lorries and workshops) was placed with Wolseley Motors Ltd. (a subsidiary of Vickers) on 30 December 1914. The Pierce-Arrow chassis (imported from the U.S.A.) used was a 14-foot wheelbase type with 30-h.p. four-cylinder engine and shaft transmission to the rear wheels. The wheels were the spoked artillery type with detachable rims and fitted with solid rubber tyres, 36-inch singles at the front and 40-inch twins at the rear. The armour protection was 5-mm. plate on thirty-two vehicles and on the remaining sixteen was increased to 0·3 in. (7½ mm.) with roofs of 0·196-in. plate (5 mm.). In addition to the 'pom pom', one Maxim machine-gun was provided, for which there were mountings on the side and rear doors and at the front.

The armoured cars were delivered by Wolseleys between March and June 1915 but the supply of 'pom poms' could not keep pace and the cars for only two batteries were equipped with guns by the end of April, when they were sent to France. The guns for a third battery were received during August and the Brigade was not fully equipped until September. Spares for the 'pom poms' were in short supply and during the Summer of 1915 there was a shortage of ammunition for the guns. In spite of these difficulties, the R.M.A. A.A. Brigade did good work, the first aircraft claimed to be shot down was on 30 April, two days after the unit was first in action, and in all around twenty enemy machines were hit and probably destroyed up to the time that the unit was re-equipped with 3-inch A.A. guns (on different mountings) during the Summer of 1917 and the 'pom pom' was withdrawn.

The 'pom poms' had a rate of fire of four rounds per second and could put up a formidable barrage. Their range was short, originally under 3000 yards, but by improvements in fuses and ammunition this was progressively increased so that eventually enemy reconnaissance and bomber aircraft

were forced to operate at over 10,000 feet, where they were far less effective.

During their time in France, the guns were frequently operated from the same positions for extended periods, and the scale of spare armoured cars turned out to be far in excess of the requirements of the Brigade and so some of them were handed over to the Royal Naval Air Service Armoured Car Division during 1915 and one car, at least, fitted with a 'pom pom' ended up in Russia with Locker–Lampson's force.

Sixteen other armoured cars, very similar in appearance to the Pierce-Arrows were built by Wolseley Motors on Peerless chain-drive chassis. These were built for Russia and delivered in 1916.

33 Sheffield-Simplex Armoured Car (built for Belgium), 1915, U.K.

The Army Motor Lorries & Waggon Co. Ltd. was formed in England at the end of 1914 to build and to repair vehicles for the Belgian Army and premises at Chelsea (London) and at Hayes, Middlesex were acquired by early 1915 for this purpose. The Chelsea works were mainly concerned with repair and reconditioning work but the factory at Hayes built fairly large numbers of specialist vehicles, including armoured cars, on new chassis.

The armoured cars were Sheffield-Simplex, the chassis supplied by the makers from their works at Tinsley, near Sheffield and the armoured hulls and turrets, to Belgian specifications, were built on at Hayes.

A conventional, but well made, quiet and smooth-running car, the Sheffield-

Simplex, had a six-cylinder engine rated at 30 h.p. The transmission, through a four-speed gear-box, was by shaft to an underslung Lanchester-type worm back axle.

The bonnet armour took advantage of the compact design of the Sheffield-Simplex engine and was low and well shaped and the hull was unusual in that the sides sloped inwards from the top. The turret with the front plates tapering to a V was somewhat like that used on some of the French Peugeot armoured cars of the same period, although offering somewhat greater protection.

Several of these armoured cars were built before the company ran into difficulties and was wound up in January 1916, when the creditors included Cammel-Laird & Co. Ltd., who had apparently supplied armour plate, and the Sheffield-Simplex Motor Works Ltd.

34 Armoured Car, 'A.C.' (Autocarrier), 1915, U.K.

The firm now known as A.C. Cars Ltd., of Thames Ditton, Surrey, has the distinction of being one of the very few companies to provide fighting vehicles to the British Army before the First World War. These were half a dozen or so of the little 'Autocarrier' single-cylinder, three-wheeled delivery vehicles which were fitted with special body work to carry either a Maxim machine-gun with crew of three or machine-gun ammunition and two men. These three-wheelers were used by a Territorial Army cyclist battalion on manoeuvres in 1910 and later and seem to have performed well.

This successful introduction to the company's products was no doubt the reason why the War Office invited Autocarriers Ltd. a few months after the outbreak of war to supply one light armoured car for experimental purposes. The chassis selected was that of the two-seater (four-wheeled) light car which had first appeared in prototype form in 1913. This used a four-cylinder 1500-c.c. proprietary engine of French design—the Fivet, with a good reputation for reliability and light in weight for its power output, rated at 10 h.p. This car is believed to have been the first on the market to use the disc type of clutch. To achieve weight saving the three-speed gear-box was incorporated in one unit with the rear axle and aluminium castings were used.

In early 1915, when a chassis was taken for use as an armoured car, it was strengthened and extended at the rear so that semi-elliptic springs could be used to replace the normal quarter elliptics. The front transverse suspension springs were reinforced. The armoured body was narrow where it enclosed the engine and lower part of the hull, but this was widened considerably into a circular structure at the rear for the crew compartment for both driver and gunners. This circular part of the hull was surmounted by a large open top rotating turret of the same diameter, mounted on only three roller bearings. A small searchlight could be carried on the turret. Provision was made for one machine-gun to be mounted.

The A.C. Armoured Car was given extensive tests by the Army in and around Aldershot during 1915. These tests were both of the armour plate (bullets were fired at it from various ranges) and of the vehicle itself. The results are not known but it would be surprising if the load imposed on a light car chassis with only a 1500-c.c. engine did not result in an unexceptional performance. No further cars of this type were built, but the question of performance aside, the Army had little need for armoured cars in 1915, since the Royal Naval Air Service Armoured Car Division provided the necessary support and was itself largely absorbed into the Army in September 1915.

35 Armoured Car, Cadillac (India pattern), 1915, India.

In India in 1914, the outbreak of war and the need to send both British and Indian troops out of the country for service on the battlefronts, accentuated the concern of the military and civil authorities with the two problems of maintaining internal security and protecting the North-West Frontier.

The decrease in the number of troops available made it essential to increase the mobility of those remaining and armoured cars were built for this purpose. One of the earliest cars to be armoured in India was a Cadillac, the armoured car shown in the drawings. This car was based in Calcutta and was used to help deal with civil disturbances. The formidable armament of two Maxim machine-guns and six or more rifles shown deployed here is unlikely ever to have been used in operations—the car was not large and it would have been impossible to make effective use of so many weapons at once. The car was only usable on made-up roads and its armour was only 5 mm. but was nevertheless valuable for use in the city as an armoured personnel carrier during riots.

36 Armoured Car, Fiat (India pattern) and Armoured Car (Workshop) Fiat (India pattern), 1915, India.

The first armoured car unit for service in the field in India—as opposed to town-based internal security units—was the 1st Armoured Motor Brigade, created in Peshawar in the Spring of 1915. This was first equipped with twelve requisitioned touring cars of five different makes and models and fitted with improvised armour of boiler plate. It was armed with early pattern Maxim 0·45-in. machine-guns, issued at first on a scale of only one per three cars.

This unit was later expanded and was joined during 1915–1916 by other Armoured Motor Brigades (with between three and six batteries each) with headquarters in Lahore and in Bannu, both also in the north-west part of India (now Pakistan). There were also independent batteries (usually of three armoured cars each) situated in important cities like Madras, Bombay, Calcutta, Secunderabad and Lucknow.

The total number of armoured cars required by this widespread organization was over sixty vehicles and the majority of these were found by acquiring touring cars of the more powerful makes and fitting them with armour—often boiler plate—in a generally similar form, although there was little standardization. The greater part of this work was undertaken by the East Indian Railway workshops at Lillooah (near Calcutta) and the North Western Railway workshops at Lahore.

In addition to private cars, some commercial chassis were also armoured in India in 1915 and the Fiats shown here are a good example. A number of armoured cars was built on 30-cwt. chassis. The design was adapted from that used for the War Office A.E.C. 'B' type Armoured Car which was constructed in the United Kingdom earlier in the year and the Beardmore $\frac{3}{16}$-in. plate used was specially supplied and sent to India.

Two Fiat armoured cars in India were experimentally equipped after the war with Marconi telegraph/telephone sets for communications over a distance. Speech was found to be possible between the cars travelling at 25 m.p.h. and, stopped, using 15-ft aerials at distances of ten miles.

To help the mobility of the armoured car batteries, a few armoured workshop vehicles were built. More than one type was built, the vehicle on a Fiat lorry chassis, shown here, being supplied towards the end of 1915 by A. Milton & Co. of Calcutta. Its equipment included a lathe, a drill and an emery grinder. Power for these was supplied by a petrol-driven electric generator. The tools for making spare parts, where necessary, were vital in an armoured car force which included such a variety of vehicles, many of them originating from European countries from which supplies of spares were no longer obtainable.

37 Armoured Car, Sizaire-Berwick ('Wind Waggon'), 1915, U.K.

The Sizaire-Berwick was a car specially designed by Maurice Sizaire to the order of F. W. Berwick, the United Kingdom agent for Sizaire-Naudin cars. Conventional in design, with a 20-h.p. four-cylinder side-valve engine,

and carried on semi-elliptic springs, the Sizaire-Berwick chassis were built in France, the bodywork being added in England. It was a high quality car, the radiator of which, perhaps not entirely unintentionally, closely resembled that of the Rolls-Royce; this was later changed after the Derby company had taken legal action.

Several Sizaire-Berwick cars were purchased by the Admiralty in early 1915 and one of these was used by the Royal Naval Air Service Armoured Car Division for an unusual experiment in the Summer of that year. R.N.A.S. Armoured Car squadrons were being withdrawn from the Western Front because trench warfare offered few opportunities for their use and were being sent to Africa and countries of the Near East where often the terrain created greater obstacles than the enemy. This Sizaire-Berwick was an experimental vehicle to try out a method of propulsion over soft sand by means of an aircraft propeller.

The French-built chassis was accordingly fitted with an aero-engine—a 110-h.p. Sunbeam with four-bladed propeller—by the F. W. Berwick Co. Ltd. at Highgate. This was rear-facing, inclined upwards slightly and was equipped with a curved propeller guard. An armoured cab for the crew—neither the bonnet at the front nor the aero-engine at the rear were armoured —was added after the car was handed over to the Admiralty. The car, known as 'Wind Waggon', was tested in England during the Summer of 1915 but was never sent to a war theatre and no other cars of this type were built. As an armoured car the Sizaire-Berwick 'Wind Waggon' was very limited in scope. One Vickers-Maxim machine-gun was mounted in the front of the hull beside the driver. There was no room for a turret which, in any event, could have had only a limited field of fire, and space for the crew armament, equipment, and fuel was very cramped. Later in the war it was found that Rolls-Royce armoured cars could be used in the Arabian desert without special equipment, other than unditching boards, although their crews had much back-breaking work in digging the cars out of soft sand.

38 Panzerkraftwagen Daimler/15
1915, Germany.

The German Army had no armoured cars at the outbreak of the First World War, but the High Command was very impressed with the performance of the Allied armoured cars encountered in the advance through Belgium and the leading German motor manufacturers of Daimler, Ehrhardt, and Büssing were each instructed to build a prototype armoured car.

The three cars were completed by the beginning of 1916 and all exhibited advanced features for the time. The Daimler was built on a conventional chassis layout with engine at the front but it had four-wheel drive and additional rear-steering controls (which, however, acted only on the front wheels) for use in emergency. The engine was a four-cylinder 80-h.p. Daimler with a gear-box giving four speeds forwards and four in reverse. The wheels were of steel construction with webbed spokes and were fitted with solid rubber tyres. Double wheels were at the rear and the front ones had

flanges added. These flanges were to help avoid sinkage in soft ground but did not maintain contact with the surface—and so affect steering—on normal roads.

The large armoured body was completely enclosed and surmounted by a fixed cylindrical turret with four machine-gun ports with 'cuckoo clock' type doors. These ports allowed a traverse for the machine-guns of 40° and 15° vertical movement. The hull had two machine-gun ports each side and one at the front and one at the rear. Three Maxim pattern MG'o8 were normally carried for use in any of these ten alternative mountings. A generous scale of observation and rifle ports was also provided in this armoured car, as can be seen from the drawings, where they are shown both open and closed. The bonnet was fully armoured and the radiator was protected by horizontal armoured louvres which could be opened and closed by means of a lever running through to the driver's position. The equipment included unditching boards carried on the hull sides and spotlights mounted on the roof.

The car was manned by a crew of eight to nine men.

Two more armoured cars of similar type were later built but preoccupation with other forms of war production prevented further efforts in this direction by the Daimler company.

39 Panzerkraftwagen Ehrhardt/15
1915, Germany.

The Ehrhardt 1915 prototype armoured car was similar in many respects to the Daimler model—it was also a front-engined four-wheel-drive vehicle with duplicate driving controls at the rear. The body and turret were of similar form to the Daimler's but the Ehrhardt 1915 model in general presented a somewhat cleaner design and the sloping front and rear of the hull were rather better-shaped and gave greater protection.

The main point of difference from the Daimler lay at the front, where the radiator was protected by vertical grilles.

Ten alternative ports in turret and hull for the three '08 pattern machine-guns normally carried were provided and in addition a pintle (otherwise used for a flag) on the front of the bonnet could be used for an anti-aircraft mounting by a dismounted crew member.

This armoured car used the four-cylinder, 85-h.p. Ehrhardt engine with a gear-box giving four speeds in both directions. The crew consisted of the commander, six gunners and one to two drivers.

40 Panzerkraftwagen Büssing/15
1915, Germany.

The Büssing firm which supplied 400 omnibuses to London before the First World War was the third German manufacturer told to develop an armoured car prototype. The Büssing design was in several respects the most interesting of the three prototypes and certainly the most impressive to look at—a massive vehicle over 30 ft long and completely symmetrical in appearance.

The 90-h.p. six-cylinder Büssing engine drove all four wheels; the gear-box provided five forward speeds and

five speeds in reverse. Front and rear driving positions were provided and all four wheels steered.

Three MG'08 pattern machine-guns were normally carried and four alternative positions in the turret and six in the hull were provided for their use. The armour was 7 mm.—protection against S-bullets at about 100 yards.

The Büssing, Daimler, and Ehrhardt 1915 armoured cars together with two improvised vehicles were formed into a unit—Panzer Kraftwagen Maschinen Gewehr Abteilung 1—early in 1916 and sent to the Western Front. After a period in the Verdun area the unit was transferred to the eastern end of the line in Alsace and near the Swiss border but static warfare was obviously unsuited to the employment of armoured cars. However, the cars were employed successfully at the battle of Kronstadt against the Roumanians and performed well in the Transylvanian Alps. This then led to over-use of the armoured car unit and it returned to Germany for rest and refitting in December 1916.

The lessons learned in Roumania were used in the design of later armoured cars. Among these were that the four-wheel steering as fitted in the Büssing was not an advantage and that the weight of the prototype vehicles—the Büssing being much the heaviest—should be reduced.

41 Autoblindata Lancia IZ, 1915, Italy.

The Lancia was the most important Italian armoured car of the First World War—it was built in some numbers and used against the Austrian and later German forces on the front on the north-east borders of Italy. Some were captured by the Germans and used to equip some armoured car units of their own, and Lancia armoured cars were used to train and equip American troops in Italy.

The basis of these cars was the Lancia 1Z 25/35-h.p. light truck chassis with pneumatic tyres, dual at the rear. The construction of the armoured cars was undertaken by the Ansaldo engineering firm, of Turin, and the vehicles were, in fact, sometimes known as Ansaldo armoured cars. The layout of the design was fairly conventional, the only really unusual feature being the small turret (with one Saint Etienne water-cooled machine-gun) superimposed on the larger turret equipped with two Saint Etienne machine-guns. The ground clearance of the Lancia armoured car was particularly good for a car of the period.

A feature also used in other Italian armoured cars was the rails, incorporating wire cutters, to enable the vehicle to pass through wire obstacles stretched across roads. The Lancia armoured car had a roomy hull (of chrome-nickel steel) and this was needed to accommodate the large crew consisting of the car commander, driver, three gunners and a mechanic.

The car weighed about 3950 kg. loaded including 25,000 rounds of ammunition. The engine of about 60 b.h.p. (35 h.p. nominal) gave a maximum speed of 70 k.p.h. and the car had a circuit of action of about 500 kms.

The 1917 model of the Lancia 1Z armoured car was almost identical in appearance to the first type except that the small turret was eliminated and the third machine-gun was mounted instead

in the back of the hull, facing rearwards.

Lancia 1Z armoured cars were long in service and some were still in use by the Italian Army in East Africa in the Second World War.

42 Davidson-Cadillac Armoured Car, 1915, U.S.A.

Major (later Colonel) R. P. Davidson, Commandant of the Northwestern Military and Naval Academy at Lake Geneva, Wisconsin, was the leading pioneer of armoured fighting vehicles in the United States. As early as 1898 he built a three-wheeled motor car mounting a Colt machine-gun: this was modified into a four-wheeled version the following year. In 1900 two four-wheeled steam powered cars, also mounting Colt automatic weapons, were built to his designs by cadets of the Northwestern Academy. Three Cadillac chassis were purchased in 1909 and 1910 and fitted with Colt machine-guns, the last two on ball and socket mountings for use against observation and dirigible balloons which were then appearing on the military scene. Two further Cadillac chassis were fitted with Colt guns in 1911 and 1912: these were equipped with both wireless and powerful searchlights. Following exhibition of one of these cars in New York, an order for four similar vehicles was placed by the Guatemalan Government and was carried out by the Cadillac Motor Car Company itself.

None of these early cars was armoured except, in some cases, for armour shields on the machine-guns. It was natural though that Davidson should eventually turn his attention to a fully armoured car and one was included in the five military automobiles he designed in 1915.

This car like most of his earlier experimental vehicles was a Cadillac, a make which was already establishing its reputation for high quality and which became widely used in the United States Army in the First World War.

The 1915 Davidson-Cadillac Armoured Car—which had the distinction of being the first fully armoured motor vehicle to be built in the U.S.A.—was similar in layout to some of the early Royal Naval Air Service armoured cars built in October 1914. Armoured all round with controllable radiator doors, the rear part had an open top, where the Colt machine-gun with an armoured shield was mounted just behind the armoured head cover for the driver. The Cadillac was a much better designed vehicle than the R.N.A.S. cars, however, (there was, of course, less urgency involved) with a lower centre of gravity and although only, like them, a conventional passenger car chassis with drive to the rear wheels, had a better cross-country performance.

The armoured car, with Colonel Davidson's other vehicles, was driven long distances by cadets of the Academy in a 1915 exercise and later in the year was tried out in U.S. Army manoeuvres It failed to arouse much interest in the potentialities of armoured cars and official encouragement of this weapon during the First World War period was only sporadic.

43   Austin-Putilov Armoured Car, 1915, Russia.

A prototype armoured car was built by the Austin Motor Co. Ltd. to the order of the Russian Imperial Government in 1914. This vehicle met with approval (Austin cars were already held in high esteem by the upper stratum of Russian society) and the first of many consignments of Austin armoured cars was produced in October of the same year.

The Austin armoured cars were built on a modified version of the 30-h.p. 'Colonial' chassis and as originally supplied had Vickers armour plate of specified thickness and twin turrets (each with one machine-gun) side by side. After delivery, however, the Russians felt that the plate was too thin and some of the cars were accordingly rebuilt with thicker armour at the Putilov armament works at Petrograd (now Leningrad). At the same time, the location of the turrets was redesigned— the cylindrical base being shortened and the turrets were staggered in order to improve the field of fire. The last was perhaps an improvement, but the new armour was, unfortunately, badly fitted in some cases and there are recorded instances of cars being put out of action by bullets penetrating between the armour and killing or wounding the crews.

The Austin-Putilov armoured cars remained generally similar in appearance to their British-built prototypes, but apart from the staggered turrets, they could be identified by the bevelled top edges of the hull running its full length, and the absence of mudguards. This same pattern of armour was, incidentally, applied also to other chassis, including, for example, a captured German Daimler 40-h.p. lorry.

The Russian armoured car sections included many soldiers who were among the best in their army and the cars were often used with great enterprise and bravery. Unfortunately, in the earlier part of the war, at least, the crews were often almost completely ignorant of mechanical matters. The Russian armoured car force was built up to nearly 200 cars by the end of 1916. Armoured cars on many different chassis were eventually acquired from various sources but the greatest single type was always the Austin, supplies of which continued up to the outbreak of the Revolution in November 1917.

44 Mgebrow-Renault Armoured Car, 1915, Russia.

This armoured car appeared in Russia in 1915. It was built on a French Renault chassis similar in most respects to that used for the French autosmitrailleuses-canons. The armour of the Russian vehicle was better designed, however, and made the best use of the dashboard radiator layout of the Renault so that the frontal armour was very effectively sloped from the front wheels right up to the roof of the hull on which the twin turrets were mounted. The turrets were placed diagonally. in the layout favoured by the Russians. One machine-gun was mounted in each turret, the barrel being protected by the projecting arms found on most armoured cars in Russian service.

Although the chassis—believed to be the 18-h.p. four-cylinder 95/160— with semi-elliptic springs was generally similar to that of the French-operated armoured cars, the wheels of the Mgebrow-Renault were of the disc type, with pneumatic tyres.

The Mgebrow-Renault probably suffered from a lack of performance,

since the load appears to have been rather heavy for the type of chassis, which in its French version had only an open-top hull and a single weapon with a shield instead of twin turrets. However, this Russian vehicle was an attractive-looking and well-protected armoured car.

45 Armoured Car, Wolseley (CP type), 1915, U.K.

The Lord Mayor of London in November 1914, opened a fund to raise £10,000 for the purchase of six 'armoured motor cars with machine-guns' for the London Mounted Brigade, a formation comprising three Territorial cavalry regiments raised in the City and County of London—1st County of London Yeomanry (The Middlesex Yeomanry), 1st City of London Yeomanry and 3rd County of London Yeomanry. The committee of the Court of Common Council entrusted with deciding on a donation from the common funds seem to have adjourned the matter and subsequently forgotten all about it, but commercial firms and private citizens responded loyally, led by Lady Strathcona and her husband Mr Howard with £1800. Rothschild's the bankers, Sir John Ellerman and Lord Mount Stephen each contributed £500, and other donations made it possible for the Lord Mayor to place an order for two armoured cars on 24 November. The order was with Vickers Ltd. for two armoured cars on Wolseley CP type chassis, Wolseley Motors Ltd. being a Vickers subsidiary. Six days earlier, the War Office had also ordered an armoured car on the same type of chassis.

The London Mounted Brigade cars were delivered on 20 July 1915 and the War Office vehicle in October 1915. The Wolseley type CP used for these armoured cars was a 30-cwt lorry chassis with 12-ft wheelbase. The engine was the four-cylinder, 3·2 litre 16/20 h.p. model. It is not clear if the War Office and London Mounted Brigade vehicles were identical, but the car shown here was fitted with disc wheels, dual at the rear, shod with Dunlop 1000 × 100 solid rubber tyres. Parsons chains were provided for use on the rear wheels.

The armoured body was built up from Vickers 0·196 in. armour plate and a revolving turret for one Vickers-Maxim machine-gun was provided in the roof.

The War Office car was lined internally with asbestos and was equipped with electric fans, so appears to have been destined for overseas service in tropical countries. The whole design of these cars was neat in appearance and careful thought was given to the equipment. Unfortunately, no record of these armoured cars after delivery seems to have survived and regimental records of the London Mounted Brigade do not mention them when the formation was sent to Egypt in 1915. The design of the hull and turret was used again for the Mercedes armoured car built by Wolseley Motors Ltd. in 1916.

46 Killen-Strait Armoured Tractor, 1915, U.K.

The Admiralty Landship Committee was set up in February 1915 to consider ways and means of producing cross-country armoured vehicles to overcome the enemy trench systems which by then had made, to all intents and purposes, most of the Royal Naval Air Service armoured cars almost useless on the Western Front.

Some of the earliest proposals were for modifications of wheeled traction engines but calculations or experiments soon disposed of these and work was concentrated on suggestions for a landship with very large wheels and a track-laying landship on the 'endless railway' principle as it was sometimes known at the time. Early theoretical figures for the big wheel landship soon proved unrealistic and this project was soon abandoned after a mock-up with 15 ft diameter wheels (even so, scaled down from the first proposals) was built and clearly demonstrated that it would be much too vulnerable a target for enemy artillery.

One of the main problems with the tracklaying landship was to obtain suitable tracks for experiment, without engaging in the time-consuming exercise of designing and building them from scratch. The American Holt Caterpillar tractor based on patents acquired from Richard Hornsby & Sons of Grantham was one of the most successful tracked vehicles then in existence, and was adapted by the British Army for towing heavy guns, but none were made available to the Landship Committee for experimental work. Work went ahead therefore using the Pedrail track which was the only British type of track available and two American makes of tractors, the Bullock Creeping Grip and the Killen-Strait, were ordered. The outcome of the experiments with the Pedrail and the Bullock tracks is described separately, but the first Killen-Strait tractor was received at the Wormwood Scrubs depot of the Royal Naval Air Service Armoured Car Division by April 1915.

The Killen-Strait tractor was an agricultural machine which had been in production at Appleton, Wisconsin, since about 1910. It was unique in having three tracks, the main driving pair at the rear and a single pivoted idle track at the front for steering. The engine was approximately in the centre of the vehicle and the driver sat behind. The Killen-Strait was tested out extensively at Wormwood Scrubs, culminating in a demonstration before Winston Churchill, Lloyd George and others on 30 June 1915. The show included the tractors overcoming various minor obstacles such as piles of railway sleepers or rails and, fitted with a naval torpedo net cutter, cutting through barbed wire entanglements.

It was known by all concerned that the Killen-Strait tractor in its existing form was not a suitable chassis for a landship but the demonstration was a great success because it showed the possibilities of improved tracklaying machines and encouraged the authorities to give continued support to the landship experiments. Following the demonstration, during July the fighting compartment (without the turret) of a R.N.A.S. Delaunay-Belleville armoured car was placed on the Killen-Strait chassis, thus creating the first tracked armoured vehicle to be built. This helped further to show what could be done, although it was never intended as a serious design.

The Killen-Strait tracks were quite good of their kind and consisted of a continuous series of steel links, joined together with 1-in. diameter pins of case-hardened steel. The treads were hardwood blocks, sheathed with heavy steel channels and bolted on to the links. Colonel R. E. B. Crompton included Killen-Strait tracks in his later designs for landships (instead of Pedrail or Bullock tracks) and also in his projected 'Emplacement Destroyer' series of 1916.

An interesting feature of the Killen-Strait tractor was the upward inclined rear of the main tracks which enabled it to reverse over obstacles which could not be crossed normally. This facility was clearly laid down in the United States patent taken out by William Strait, the inventor, in 1912. There was subsequently much argument as to who first thought of the upturned bow design used in 'Mother'. There is no doubt at all that the R.N.A.S. Killen-Strait was the first armoured vehicle with tracks in this form and it seems more than probable that the adaptation of this idea in 'Mother' had its origin in the demonstrations of the Killen–Strait.

47 **Pedrail Landship,** 1915, U.K.

The design of the tracked landship, proposals for which, together with a 'big wheel' landship, were put before the Landship Committee, was entrusted to Colonel R. E. B. Crompton, a distinguished engineer who had seen active service in the Boer War in 1900.

Before Crompton's appointment to the Landship Committee, which took effect on 1 March 1915, some research had already been undertaken by Commodore Murray Sueter, R.N., Director of the Air Department of the Admiralty which controlled the Armoured Car Division of the R.N.A.S.

In examining the possibility of building a full-tracked armoured vehicle for the Royal Naval Air Service to restore the mobility to the armoured car squadrons on the Western Front it was soon discovered that Pedrail tracks were the only ones available for use. These were evolved for a small cross-country horse-drawn truck, built by Pedrail Transport Ltd. of Fulham, London. These were single wide tracks with the truck body supported on external rails.

A design for a tracked armoured car was roughed out by Commodore Sueter using as a basis some of his knowledge of the design of submarines and data on armour and armament weights of the R.N.A.S. turreted (wheeled) armoured cars. This worked out at a landship of around 30 ft long, and estimated to weigh 24 tons and be within the capacity of most main bridges. These ideas were turned into general arrangement drawings by Mr Diplock, Director of Pedrail Transport Ltd. These showed a landship 38 ft long and 12 ft 6 in. wide, running on two single Pedrail tracks in tandem, since, although scaled up tracks could be built, one track for a 30–40 ft machine was out of the question. Each Pedrail track was driven by a 46-h.p. Rolls-Royce engine mounted so that each unit-engine and track was on a steerable turntable and the estimated turning radius of the machine was 65 ft. The driver occupied a raised position in the centre of the vehicle: the top of his cupola was raised 3 ft 3 in. above the level of the rest of the hull roof, which was 7 ft 3 in. high. The crew was eight men and the armament proposed was

one 12-pdr. gun. The loaded weight was worked out at 25 tons, with a ground pressure of 12 lb. per square inch. These drawings were completed on 28 February 1915 and submitted to Colonel Crompton shortly after his appointment to the Landship Committee. Crompton approved the design, which was laid before the full Landship Committee on 4 March. Some alterations may have been incorporated, but a model was constructed and this, when shown to Winston Churchill at the Admiralty on 20 March, together with a model of the rival 'big wheel' landship design, decided the First Lord to order twelve Pedrail landships and six 'big wheel' landships.

At this stage, although the mechanical specification and overall dimensions do not seem to have been altered, the tactical use of the landships had evidently been given further consideration, because they were now stipulated to carry a trench-assaulting party of seventy infantrymen (later reduced to fifty) with machine-guns and ammunition and the 12-pdr. gun was omitted from the design.

Plans went ahead for production of the twelve tracked landships; Foden Ltd. were appointed as contractors and Rolls-Royce, who had already received a preliminary order for three sets of engines (two engines per landship) were instructed to go ahead and produce engines for all twelve vehicles. The engines, incidentally, were basically of the normal 40/50-h.p. Silver Ghost pattern and to avoid complicated redesign of the components were supplied on shortened car chassis complete with clutch and gear-box. This had made them difficult to incorporate into the design, although the R.N.A.S. wanted Rolls-Royce engines because of their excellent performance in armoured cars.

During the time that construction of the main chassis and engines of the landship was under way, research was carried on into devices for the clearance of barbed wire, trench cutting ploughs to enable the landships to dig themselves in and grenade throwing apparatus with which it was felt the landship should be equipped.

Crompton felt it necessary to go to France, following his appointment, to see for himself the conditions under which the landships would have to operate and did so on 21 April. On his return he redesigned the landship as an articulated vehicle so that it would be able to negotiate some of the narrow bends and corners in roads close to the front line. Two equal halves, each 22 ft long and joined by a universal coupling were proposed so that the steering radius was reduced to 42 ft. He also redesigned the side armour so that it could be swung outwards in sections to enable the crew to remove barbed wire entanglements from under cover. In the meantime, however, it appears that manufacture of at least the first of the twelve tracked landships went ahead on the basis of the original design.

It was known that the Pedrail tracks were far from ideal in design or construction for heavy machines and American Bullock Creeping Grip Tractors and Killen-Strait tractors were ordered for experimental purposes. Crompton redesigned his articulated landship during May with Bullock tracks, reducing the turning radius to 40 ft. Also, a special set of lengthened

Bullock tracks, with a base of 9 ft was ordered from America in the same month. The Bullock tractors were found to be satisfactory enough operated normally, but when two were coupled together for preliminary experiments for the articulated landships it was soon evident that the twisting stresses imposed on the couplings created considerable problems.

Colonel Crompton was not discouraged, however, and when new requirements were received from the War Office at the beginning of July to abandon the infantry carrying type and design a gun-equipped landship he still stuck to the articulated layout. The new requirements were, in fact, a reversion to the original concept by Sueter and Diplock although this time it does not seem to have been finally decided whether to use guns of 3-pdr. calibre (or bigger) or 'pom pom' automatic weapons. The overall height of 9 ft 6 in. of the first of Crompton's gun-carrying landships with two turrets on each half was reduced to 7 ft 6 in. by eliminating the top turrets and also lowering the total weight from 28 tons to 26 tons and the height was even further reduced to only 6 ft in a later design using special Killen-Strait tracks.

By July most of the Rolls-Royce engines for the landships had been completed and some progress had been made with the parts for the landships themselves but then the Metropolitan Carriage, Wagon & Finance Co., to whom the contract had been transferred from Fodens in April, asked to be relieved of this work. The original contract had, in any case, by this time been reduced from the original twelve to only one for experimental work.

Also, by now Sueter and Commander F. L. N. Boothby, his Officer Commanding Armoured Cars, were becoming rather impatient with Colonel Crompton. They were in urgent need of a machine on which to commence training the men of the three new squadrons (Nos. 20, 21 and 22) of the R.N.A.S. which had been raised to operate the landships. They also felt, although respecting Crompton's considerable ability, that not only was the articulated type of landship, on which he was concentrating his efforts, likely to take a long time to perfect—particularly the coupling problem—but was also too complicated and heavy. Mr E. Tennyson d'Eyncourt, Director of Naval Construction and Chairman of the Landship Committee, was converted to this point of view and agreed to give instructions for what amounted in effect to one half of an articulated landship with Bullock tracks to be built for experimental purposes. This work was given at the end of July to William Foster & Co., who had taken over the contract for the sole remaining landship of the original order for a dozen.

Although Colonel Crompton's appointment with the Landship Committee terminated on 31 August 1915 he continued to work, on his own, on further designs of articulated landships, reaching a 'Mark VII' model by October and only finally abandoning landship work and turning instead to 'Emplacement Destroyers' (4·5-in. howitzer armoured carriers) after the trials of 'Mother' had evidently proved successful and led to the acceptance of Wilson's design.

One Pedrail Landship was finally

built by Stothert & Pitt Ltd., of Bath, using mostly parts already made to the original contract, although employing two 100-h.p. Aster engines instead of Rolls-Royce engines and a frame constructed by Messrs William Arrol. Apart from this, the chassis built, and shown here, was very much like the original rigid frame concept. With some modifications this vehicle was completed for the Trench Warfare Department of the Ministry of Munitions and was intended to carry a flame-thrower. Its final weight was about 32 tons and it achieved the commendable speed of 15 m.p.h. on trials on Salisbury Plain. It was never used in action and after the war was dumped at Bovington Camp, where it was known as the 'Porton Tractor' and, its historical significance as an earlier concept than the successful tanks not properly appreciated, was broken up in 1923.

48 **Armoured Car, Jeffery-Quad,** 1915, U.S.A.

The Jeffery-Quad was a four-wheel drive truck with four-wheel brakes and steering on all wheels. Large numbers were built in the United States during the First World War for the Allies for use as load carriers and gun tractors and, later, for the U.S. Army.

In 1914, Jerry De Cou, factory superintendent of the Thomas B. Jeffery Co., designed and built an armoured car on the Jeffery-Quad chassis. Following this two other different types of armoured cars were also constructed, again with armour provided by the Bethlehem Steel Corporation. One of the three types had an octagonal central superstructure (with large opening flaps for weapons) and enclosed wheels; another had a comparatively low flat-topped hull with a circular revolving turret and the third type, known as Armored Car No. 1 to the U.S. Ordnance Corps in 1915, had a tall hull surmounted by a turret in the centre, with a second turret stepped down lower at the rear. The second car mentioned above was used by the U.S. Army on the Mexican border in 1916 during the rising by Pancho Villa and also, possibly, the third type.

These cars were built as experimental vehicles only, but yet a fourth type, something of a cross between the second and the third models, was manufactured in some numbers for the British Army.

This armoured car had a single rotating turret in the centre, but this was supplemented by four small semi-circular sponsons (each with two loop-holes) on the hull sides. The vehicle was provided with a duplicate steering wheel and driving controls at the rear and there were raised armoured driver's cabs both in front of and behind the turret. Over the cover for the engine (which was in the normal position at the front) were two curved bars to engage and cut wire obstacles. The suspension consisted of semi-elliptic leaf springs at front and rear and the wheels had solid rubber tyres. The cars weighed about $6\frac{1}{2}$ tons and the 40-h.p. Buda four-cylinder engine gave them a maximum speed of about 20 m.p.h., both forward and reverse.

Jeffery armoured cars of this pattern were imported into Canada by the Canada Cycle & Motor Co. Ltd. of Toronto (makers of Russell trucks) and they may actually have been assembled

there also, because identical armoured cars to the Jeffery-Quad appeared before the end of 1915 described as 'Russell armoured cars'.

From whatever source—the United States or Canada—they came, the British Army acquired a quantity of Jeffery-Quad armoured cars. The exact number cannot be ascertained, but in late 1917 forty had been sent to the British Army in India and there were twenty-two in Ireland in 1919. The cars in India (reduced to about nineteen at the end of the war) were used to equip one of the newly formed Armoured Car Companies of the Royal Tank Corps in October 1921 and some of these were kept going—more or less—until about Autumn 1924. Spares were in short supply, however and some cars had to be 'cannibalized' to provide parts for the others. The punishing roads of the North-West Frontier of India (as it then was—now Pakistan) showed that the Jeffery-Quads were not strongly enough built but somehow or other the remaining cars were sold by auction in early 1925.

The original models of the Jeffery armoured cars carried four or more Benét-Mercié machine-guns but the cars in Ireland and India normally had only one 0·303-in. Vickers machine-gun, mounted in the turret.

49 Armoured Car, Leyland, 1915, U.K.

Vehicles built by Leyland Motors Ltd. formed nearly 10 per cent of all the British Army lorries in service at the end of the First World War. The Leyland three-tonner was a sturdy and well built lorry (and one which remained popular with civilian operators for many years after the war) and this type of chassis was chosen for the four heavy armoured cars forming the core of the 1st Armoured Motor Battery, Motor Machine Gun Corps, which was raised towards the end of 1915.

The cost of this battery, commanded by Major Sir John Willoughby, was borne by private subscription—it was formed for service in German East Africa and was intended to be self-contained as far as possible and so had a generous supply of transport, including four Leyland 3-ton lorries, a workshop lorry, about seven cars or light lorries and some eighteen Douglas motor-cycles.

The chassis used for the armoured cars was the 13 ft 11 in. wheelbase 3-ton model (which became known as the 'R.A.F. type' because of its wide use by the Royal Flying Corps and later the Royal Air Force) with semi-elliptic leaf springs at front and rear.

For the armoured cars, projections on the underside were limited to the minimum so that they had a quite good ground clearance. The engine was a four-cylinder unit developing 30–40 h.p. at 1,000 r.p.m. Transmission was via a four-speed gear-box with final drive by shaft to a differential on the rear axle. The wheels—the rear ones dual and of larger diameter than the front—were pressed steel discs and solid rubber tyres were fitted all round. The armoured hull was built up of Beardmore armour plates of $\frac{3}{16}$-in. and $\frac{1}{4}$-in. thickness. The fact that this was far from being a mass production order is shown by small differences in the fitting of the armour in all four vehicles.

The armament was two Vickers 0·303-in. water-cooled machine-guns, one mounted in a revolving turret on the hull roof and the other in an aperture in the hull rear.

Equipment on the cars included a searchlight mounted on the turret roof and a semaphore arm on the hull top. For aid in getting out of soft ground a long unditching board was carried, attached to the left side of the hull. (On active service, wide flanges to help prevent sinkage were added to the front wheels.)

The crew of the Leyland heavy armoured cars was six men, one of whom acted as second driver to operate the duplicate steering wheel for driving in reverse in emergency.

The 1st Armoured Motor Battery was sent to German East Africa in 1916 but in country where even the much lighter Rolls-Royce armoured cars infrequently went into top gear, the heavy Leylands were helpless. Although they had been designed with more care and forethought than most contemporary heavy armoured cars they only rarely encountered the enemy, and they had little influence on the campaign.

50 'Little Willie', 1915, U.K.

Instructions to Mr William Tritton of William Foster and Co. Ltd. of Lincoln, assisted by Lieutenant W. G. Wilson of the Royal Naval Air Service, to design a small landship with Bullock tracks were given when the main stream of landship development and also parallel experiments seemed unlikely to lead to a successful conclusion in time to play a useful part in the war.

The Chairman of the Landship Committee (Mr E. Tennyson d'Eyncourt) gave the order for the experimental vehicle on 29 July 1915. Work on what was known at first as the 'Tritton Machine' was commenced immediately; a full sized wooden mock-up was completed by 26 August and the machine itself shortly afterwards. First trials took place near Lincoln early in September 1915.

The 'Tritton Machine' was, in essence, like one half of the articulated gun-equipped landship with Bullock tracks, designs for which had already been drawn up by Colonel Crompton. The hull was a rectangular armoured box (boiler plate was, in fact, used) carried on tracks of shorter length than the body and surmounted by a turret. The armament was to be a 2-pdr. gun and several machine-guns although the real turret was never fitted, the equivalent weight being represented by a dummy.

The 'Creeping Grip' tracks ordered specially from the Bullock Tractor Co. of Chicago were longer than the normal type used on the agricultural tractors tried out in earlier landship experiments. They were supplied as a unit complete with track frames and wheels and had seven small road wheels and five guide wheels compared with the four road wheels and three guides of the standard type.

No attempt was made to introduce the Rolls-Royce engines on shortened car chassis, some of which had already been completed for the twelve Pedrail landships: this would have complicated the design and a 105-h.p. Daimler six-cylinder engine, gear-box and differential of the type well known to Tritton

from use in Foster's wheeled tractors, was used to power the 'Tritton Machine'. Transmission was to the centre of the track frames, which were pivoted, and thence by chain drive to the track sprockets at the rear.

There was little data on full tracked vehicles to go on—most of the tracked agricultural tractors of the period, including the Bullock tractors were, in modern terms, 'half-tracks' with the front end supported on wheels. Tritton made provision for a pair of wheels steerable on the Ackermann principle, at the rear of the machine. These wheels were intended to improve the balance, assist in crossing trenches and aid the normal steering of the vehicle, which was by braking on either track.

The Tritton Machine was the first vehicle to be designed and completed as a landship, or tank, but was not entirely successful because the lengthened Bullock tracks were found to be of poor quality and were still too short and a trench of only 4-foot width could be crossed, when the current War Office requirement was for a 5-foot trench.

These shortcomings were foreseen and a second type was drawn up by Tritton, assisted by Wilson, even before the first was completed. This had improved tracks, specially designed, and new track frames (about 3 ft longer) and running gear, although the other features remained the same.

After trials, the 'Tritton Machine' was rebuilt with the new track frames and tracks, and emerged in its new form —now without the dummy turret—early in December 1915. This historic vehicle has fortunately been preserved in the Royal Armoured Corps Tank Museum at Bovington, Dorset where close examination will reveal redundant bolt or rivet holes associated with the earlier equipment.

The modified 'Tritton Machine', or 'Little Willie' as it then become known, was much better than in its original form but was unable to meet new War Office obstacle-crossing requirements, which had been again revised, and was soon overshadowed by the new machine, 'Big Willie'.

51 Automitrailleuse White, 1915, France.

The French Government began receiving, in 1915, supplies of trucks built by the White Motor Co. of Cleveland, Ohio and by the end of the same year the first twenty armoured cars were constructed in France on White chassis.

The White was a fairly conventional chassis with a 35-h.p. four-cylinder water-cooled engine with drive to the rear wheels, although in the armoured car duplicate steering controls were fitted for driving backwards in emergency. The maximum speed of this 6-ton vehicle was 28 m.p.h. and the radius of action was about 155 miles.

The normal crew carried was four men and the armament consisted of one 37-mm. gun and one Hotchkiss machine-gun, or alternatively machine-guns only. The two mountings were on opposite sides of the turret, which was of distinctive design and liberally equipped with observation ports.

By the end of the First World War the French Army had no less than 205 White armoured cars—more than three times the combined total of Renaults and Peugeots. This large supply led

France, like Britain, to retain many war-time armoured cars in service after the war and some White armoured cars, modernized in details but still essentially the same in appearance, were in action in the earlier years of the Second World War.

52 'Mother', 1916, U.K.

At the same time that the 'Tritton Machine' was being re-designed, Lieutenant W. G. Wilson was working on an entirely new model of landship to meet the new War Office requirements to cross an 8-foot wide trench and climb a parapet 4 ft 6 in. high. In this machine, known at first as 'Big Willie', the famous lozenge-shaped profile with tracks running round the top of the hull was introduced for the first time. It was said that the lower curve of the track was derived from a section of the perimeter of a big wheel of a diameter sufficient to cross the trench width stipulated by the War Office. This data may conceivably have dictated the height of the front idler wheel and the overall length of the machine, but the use of an upturned track profile for crossing obstacles had already been demonstrated in the Killen-Strait tractor and in the design of the Nesfield-McFie landship, a model of which was submitted to the Admiralty in June 1915. Be this as it may, the 'Wilson Machine', or 'H.M. Landship Centipede' as it was also known, was an effective and impressive vehicle.

To avoid the high centre of gravity attendant on a turret on top of the hull, the main armament—two Naval 6-pdr. guns—was carried in half-turrets (called sponsons—a Naval term) projecting from each side of the hull. The same power unit as 'Little Willie' was retained, together with the same type of track and also the tail wheels.

The 'Wilson Machine' was built by William Foster & Co. Ltd. at Lincoln and first ran on 16 January 1916, only just over a month after the rebuilt 'Little Willie'. It easily excelled its smaller relative in comparative trials of both machines and at Hatfield Park, Hertfordshire negotiated without difficulty barbed wire entanglements and representations of British- and German-type trenches which were specially constructed to test the machine's ability.

The 'Wilson Machine', 'H.M.L.S. Centipede' or 'Big Willie' (as it was nicknamed, in contrast with the improved 'Tritton Machine') also acquired the nickname of 'Mother' and as the progenitor of all the British heavy tanks of the First World War this, appropriately, is the name by which it is nearly always known today.

53 Sheffield-Simplex Armoured Car (built for Russia), 1916, U.K.

An order was placed early in the war by the Russian Imperial Government for Sheffield-Simplex 30-h.p. vehicles for military use, including light lorries, ambulances and cars, and the first contract was completed by the beginning of November 1914. Also ordered were some armoured cars, which were probably completed in the early part of 1915.

These armoured cars were very similar to the Sheffield-Simplex cars built for Belgium, but instead of a single turret they had the twin turrets favoured by the Russians. The engine and hull armour were in nearly all respects the same for both Russian and Belgian vehicles.

This early 1915 type was superseded by the generally similar but improved model which is shown in the drawings. This vehicle probably went into production for the Russian Government in the latter part of 1915. Certainly, some cars of this newer type had been completed by January 1916.

The 1916 Russian Sheffield-Simplex armoured car used the well proven 30-h.p. chassis. The earlier armoured cars had the standard touring car size wheels (although they were dual at the rear) but in the 1916 pattern larger diameter wheels with 1020 × 120-mm. tyres were fitted to take the heavier load of some 5 tons. These were also dual at the rear and all were filled with Rubberine. The chassis used for the armoured cars differed from standard only in the wheels, although after tests with the prototype the propeller shaft and back axles were strengthened.

The twin turrets, fitted somewhat farther forward than on the earlier Russian model, were equipped with one Maxim gun each. The gunners sat on Brooks' motor-cycle saddles which revolved with the turrets. The hull armour consisted of steel plates which were screwed on to a beechwood framework attached to the chassis. Access to the engine was good: the top plate was hinged upwards and both side armour panels could be removed completely. Vision ports were provided for the driver and the co-driver in the front hull plate and a small searchlight was mounted behind the left-hand portion. There also were two ports in the rear of the hull and one at either side, near the front. The one on the driver's side (incorporated in the door) was fitted with a driving mirror on its inside. All projecting parts inside the hull were padded. In accordance with specification, all instructions were printed in Russian and the speedometer was calibrated in versts.

The work of armouring the Russian Sheffield-Simplex cars was carried out by Thomas Piggott & Co. Ltd. at Birmingham between 1915 and 1917 until the Revolution broke out in Russia and so delivery of the last vehicles was withheld.

54 Mack Armoured Car (New York National Guard), 1916, U.S.A.

This Mack armoured car, together with two other similar vehicles on White and Locomobile chassis formed the nucleus of the fighting strength of the 1st Armored Motor Battery, New York National Guard. The whole equipment of this battery, which was raised on 18 March 1916 and included seventy-two motor-cycles, two trucks and a staff car as well as the three armoured cars, was paid for by a group of wealthy and patriotic New York citizens.

The Mack armoured car, constructed by the International Motor Company of New York, had a straightforward open top armoured hull, somewhat better in design than many of its contemporaries in that the top half was sloped inwards to improve its ballistic properties. Two Colt machine-guns with curved shields were mounted staggered in the rear part where they had a good field of fire. The engine air intake at the front was protected by adjustable shutters. The chassis was

basically that of the Mack 2-ton, 144-in. wheelbase truck, with worm drive and dual rear wheels while the tyres were formed of solid rubber blocks. A big vehicle, the Mack armoured car was 19 ft 8 in. long, 6 ft 6 in. wide and 8 ft 4 in. high (to top of gun shields) and weighed $4\frac{1}{2}$ (short) tons. The equipment included a Gray and Davis 10-in. searchlight. The Locomobile and White armoured cars were very much the same as the Mack in appearance, although the Locomobile, using a six-cylinder passenger car chassis, had smooth (continuous) solid tyres and horizontal radiator grilles. The White was based on a $1\frac{1}{2}$-ton truck chassis. The armoured hulls, from the radiator armour backwards, were identical in all three cars and were built by the Carnegie Steel Corporation.

The 1st Armored Motor Battery was used on the Mexican border in 1916 but the cars became well known after the United States entered the war against Germany in the following April by being used in demonstrations and war parades. However, the 1st Armored Motor Battery was disbanded in November 1917: it was not absorbed into the regular army which, at that time, had little use for armoured cars.

55 Fiat Armoured Car, 1916, Russia.

Among the many makes of foreign motor chassis used for military purposes by the Russians were Italian-built Fiats. This make was also one of the far lesser number of models used for the basis of armoured cars.

The Russian Fiat armoured car which appeared in 1916 used a conventional touring car chassis with pneumatic tyres, which at the rear were doubled to take the increased weight.

The armour, which appears to have been fitted in Russia was broadly similar in layout to that of the Putilov-armoured Austins, although the Fiat's shorter wheelbase apparently led to the right-hand turret being the one offset to the rear, to give the driver more room and also provide a door at this point.

The armament, as with several other Russian armoured cars of the period, consisted of one water-cooled machine-gun in each turret. To protect the vulnerable water jackets on the barrels of the weapons, the Fiat armoured cars usually, but not always, had the characteristic armour 'arms' projecting from the turret face.

Later versions of Russian Fiat armoured cars had various changes including a different shaped turret base and, later still, detachable type disc wheels were used instead of the artillery type with detachable rims. Among the armoured cars placed at the disposal of the British Royal Naval Air Service armoured car force in July 1917, following losses of equipment, were eight Fiat armoured cars and one of these, at least, had disc wheels with pneumatic tyres and a modified hull with a large turret, apparently fixed.

56 Daimler Armoured Lorry, 1916, Ireland.

Many armoured cars of the First World War were improvisations, but very few can have been constructed as quickly as this vehicle which appeared on the streets of Dublin in 1916.

The rising in Ireland, which began on the Easter Monday of 1916, manifested itself in guerrilla activities all over the country. The main centre of fighting was, however, in the capital, where snipers made the streets of Dublin dangerous for British soldiers on patrol and engaged in convoying valuables and supplies. The rising was nearly over in Dublin by 29 April but it was, nevertheless, decided to construct an armoured car for convoy and patrol work. Authority was given on the morning of 30 April for the work to be done and the lorry which had already been chosen to be converted into an armoured car was driven to the Great Southern Railway works at Inchicore and the job was completed by 6.30 p.m. on the same day.

The resulting vehicle was bizarre in appearance and, as the drawings show, its origin in a locomotive engineering works was apparent. The lorry itself was commandeered from Guinness' brewery and was a German-built Daimler 3-ton shaft-driven vehicle, normally used for carrying supplies of beer. The conversion was simple—an 'armoured' body assembled from locomotive smoke-boxes was mounted on the lorry platform; flat plates were used to protect the radiator and the sides and front of the driver's cab and a locomotive cab roof was used for overhead cover. Rifle loopholes were cut in the sides of the cylindrical body and, to confuse snipers, dummy loopholes were painted in other places. The boiler-plate used as armour was not proof against rifle bullets at close range (although the curvature of the cylinder made it more effective) but when the lorry did come under fire it gave at least some protection to its occupants.

Another lorry of the same type was

also armoured in Dublin at about the same time—this one again used loco-motive boiler plate but arranged as a single rectangular structure covering both the lorry platform and the driver's cab.

When the emergency was over it is believed the lorries were returned to the brewery and their armour to the Inchi-core railway workshops for use again in constructing locomotives.

57 Autocanon 47 mm.—Renault, 1916, France.

The first lorry-mounted gun to go into action in France in the First World War was probably the British Com-mander C. R. Samson's 3 pdr. on a L.G.O.C. 'B' type chassis, which was constructed to Royal Naval Air Ser-vice designs by the French shipyard Forges et Chantiers de France at Dun-kirk in October 1914.

The French equivalent of this weapon appeared during the course of 1916 and consisted of a gun of the same calibre as Samson's on a Renault lorry chassis with solid tyres. Whereas the R.N.A.S. vehicle was unarmoured and the gun mounted fairly high on the lorry plat-form the French Autocanon 47 mm. was fully armoured and the gun was mounted low between the rear wheel arches in the body of the vehicle. The only disadvantage of this lower mount-ing was that the gun did not have a forward field of fire because the driver's cab was in the way.

These Autocanons, like their British equivalents (following Samson's proto-type, built on Seabrook chassis) were manned by naval personnel—Fusiliers Marins—and were also used as mobile

light artillery to run up and down be-hind the lines, attacking such targets as presented themselves.

58 Panzerkraftwagen Mannes-mann-Mulag, 1916, Germany.

The Mannesmann-Mulag, built by the Aachen firm, was a fairly conventional lorry supplied to the German Army as a load carrier in the 1914–18 War. The drive was by shaft to a differential on the rear axle and the wheels, shod with solid rubber tyres, were carried on semi-elliptic springs at front and rear.

This chassis was used for a heavy armoured car built about 1916. The vehicle was, in fact, an armoured per-sonnel carrier rather than a true fighting vehicle because it had no turret or pro-vision for the permanent mounting of armament, although ports were pro-vided at sides, front, and rear for the use of crew weapons—machine-guns or small arms. Like most other German armoured cars, the Mannesmann-Mulag was fully equipped, including powerful spotlights at front and rear.

59 Armoured Car, Mercedes-Wol-seley, 1916, U.K.

This armoured car started life as a pri-vate motor car—a 'limousine with de-tachable brougham top'—belonging to Mr James Hainsworth Ismay, of Iwerne Minster House, Dorset. The chassis was a 1911 model 45-h.p. Mercedes with a 4·1-litre, four-cylinder Knight sleeve-valve engine.

In July 1916 the conversion to an armoured car was effected. The main change to the chassis was in the intro-duction of dual tyres at the rear to take the increased weight. The work of fitting the armour was undertaken by Wolseley Motors Ltd., and it is noticeable that the design of the revolving turret is identical to that of the 1915 Wolseley CP type armoured cars.

Nothing appears to have been recorded concerning the employment of this armoured car, but, although it is unlikely to have been sent overseas, it may well have been intended for either the Hampshire Carabiniers Yeomanry or the Dorset Yeomanry, with which Territorial regiments Mr J. H. Ismay served in 1914–16.

60 Autoblindata Bianchi, 1916, Italy.

S. A. Automobile e Velocipedi Eduardo Bianchi, of Milan, was founded in 1899: by the time of the First World War which Italy joined on the side of the Western Allies in 1915, Bianchi cars had established a reputation as well-built orthodox vehicles of good quality. As in other countries, a car of this kind was the obvious choice for the basis of an armoured car.

The first Bianchi armoured car was built about 1912 and was similar in most respects to the slightly earlier Isotta-Fraschini. About three years later an updated version of the Bianchi armoured car with revised armour and equipment was built. This model had pneumatic tyres, dual at the rear. The back wheels were covered and, more unusually, the front wheels also were protected, by close-fitting semicircular guards which moved with them. This car was experimental only and in 1916 was built the modified version illustrated here.

The Autoblindata Bianchi (1916) was an open top vehicle, armed with two water-cooled machine-guns, one in a centrally pivoted mounting with a shield, and the other projecting through the rear of the hull.

The hull was, to just above the driver's visor level, identical with that of the earlier model with a turret. The cutting down of the hull in this way, and eliminating the turret considerably decreased the weight and improved the performance of the 1916 model. To clear road obstructions like wire an angle steel frame was carried right over the car from low down in front of the front wheels to beyond the rear hull machine-gun. Equipment carried included unditching boards on the right-hand side of the hull and—a feature of Italian armoured car units—a folded bicycle.

61 Tank, Mark I, 1916, U.K.

'Mother's' performance on demonstrations in January and February 1916 convinced the military and Government spectators of the potential value of this new weapon and forty machines were ordered early in February, an order which was shortly afterwards increased to 100. 'Mother' was built of boiler plate (and is identifiable in pictures by the close pitch rivets) but the production machines were, of course, to be of armour plate varying from 12 mm. to 6 mm. in thickness, although otherwise identical to their prototype. However, it was decided to change the armament in half of the machines produced to machine-guns only to enable them to attack infantry more effectively —these ones had a total of four Vickers water-cooled machine-guns in the side sponsons and one Hotchkiss machine-gun.

By this time the name 'tank' had come into general currency. This had its origin in the code name 'Water Carrier for Mesopotamia' used in William Foster & Co's works for 'Mother'—this soon became shortened to 'tank'. Less revealing of its purpose than 'landship', this name was later officially adopted, the first production machines becoming Tanks, Mark I. The machine-gun armed tanks were then called 'Females', the ones with 6-pdr. guns being 'Males'.

The first order for tanks was divided between William Foster & Co. to build twenty-five and the Metropolitan Carriage, Wagon & Finance Co. at Wednesbury—seventy-five. This order for 100 was increased in April 1916 to 150.

The battle in which the tanks, manned by the newly raised Heavy Section, Machine Gun Corps, first took part was unfortunately an ill-chosen one, with unsuitable ground and when numbers were insufficient to take full advantage of the element of surprise. This was the battle of Flers-Courcellette, part of the great Somme offensive which was then failing, when forty-nine Tanks, Mark I went into action on 15 September 1916 although only a few reached their objectives. Despite the inexperience of the crews, breakdowns through mechanical trouble or bad ground, the results achieved were encouraging enough to bring orders for further tank production.

62 Char Schneider, 1916, France.

The development of trench warfare on the Western Front in 1914–15 prompt-ed the invention in France, as in England, of devices to overcome machine-guns and barbed wire. Rollers and wheeled tractors of the agricultural type for crushing or cutting through obstacles were tried out and in January 1915 the armaments firm of Schneider et Cie. of Le Creusot obtained two versions of the successful American track-laying Holt tractor. One was the semi-tracked and more common type—already in use by the British Army for gun towing—with tracks at the rear and steering wheels at the front and the other was the smaller 'Baby' type with tracks only. The latter was found to be more handy for use as a cross-country vehicle. A demonstration was given before the President of the French Republic on 16 June 1915; the Schneider concern were encouraged to prepare designs for an armed and armoured version (tracteur armé et blindé).

Eugène Brillié was the designer employed on this work, and he was responsible for the introduction of the nose piece and the tail skid later used in the production machines. One of the armoured Holt tractors was fitted with a machine-gun but the idea was that the main function of these vehicles should be to destroy and cross barbed wire and it was intended that they should be fitted at the front with a wire-cutting device invented by J. L. Bréton, a member of the Chambre des Députés.

An official order for ten machines was given to Schneiders on 15 December 1915. At this time Colonel Baptiste Estienne, who for over a year had been urging the French G.Q.G. to develop armoured tracklaying vehicles to overcome the stalemate of trench warfare, was put in touch with the Schneider firm. He was able to place his own ideas and practical experience of warfare at the disposal of Monsieur Brillié and changes were introduced into the designs.

Two prototype Schneider machines, including the one fitted with a machine-gun, which also had extended tracks, were demonstrated at Vincennes on 21 February 1916. Both did well in crossing trenches and barbed wire and 400 of similar type to the machine-gun-armed model were ordered on 25 February, delivery to be made before 25 November. At this stage the inclusion of a 75-mm. gun in the armament was evidently decided on.

The first batch of vehicles—'tracteurs Estienne', later known as 'Chars d'assault' or simply 'Chars' were delivered in September 1916, in the same month that British tanks were first used in action on the Somme. The Schneider tank consisted, essentially, of an armoured box with a pointed nose placed on a lengthened Holt Caterpillar chassis. The suspension was made up of two bogie units (three wheels and four wheels, respectively) each side, sprung on coil springs. The engine was a 70-h.p. four-cylinder type mounted near the front, to the left of the centre line, with the radiator in front of it. An air intake grille was incorporated in the nose glacis plate. The three-speed gearbox was at the rear and the track driving sprockets were at the rear of the track. The maximum speed attainable was 5 m.p.h. and steering was by the clutch and brake method. One short 75-mm. gun was fitted in a sponson on the right-hand side of the hull with one Hotchkiss machine-gun further back on the same side and one Hotchkiss machine-gun in the middle of the hull on the

other side. Ninety rounds of ammunition were carried for the gun and 4000 rounds for the machine-guns. Six men made up the crew, the officer in command being also the driver.

Faults which became apparent in the Schneider tanks in training and later in action—for the first time on 16 April 1917—included poor ventilation and vision arrangements and inadequate armour, danger in action of fire in the internal petrol tanks and lack of egress on the left-hand side. Changes to add extra doors, modify the petrol tanks and add additional $5\frac{1}{2}$-mm. plates to the main vertical surfaces (which were 11·4 mm. at the sides) to give protection against the German 'K' bullet were recommended but were carried out at best only slowly and spasmodically and not all tanks received all or indeed any modifications.

The defects in the French heavy tanks led Colonel Estienne to advocate the acquisition of British Mark V or later model tanks in exchange for Renault light tanks, which were highly successful and in quantity production. This was done and seventy-seven Tanks, Mark V* were received by the French before the Armistice, but some Schneiders were still in service when the war ended.

63 **Char Saint-Chamond**, 1916, France.

The Char Schneider was intended to be the standard French heavy tank and an order was placed for 400 of them on 25 February 1916. However, Monsieur J. L. Bréton, of the French Government department responsible for war inventions, gave authority for the firm Forges et Aciéries de la Marine et d'Homécourt, at Saint Chamond near Lyon, to design another tank, larger and better-armed than the Schneider. Both departmental and industrial jealousy were involved because this step was taken without full knowledge of the Army and neither Joffre, the Commander-in-Chief, nor Estienne, the leading military expert on the subject were consulted and there was no co-operation with the Schneider firm.

The design of the Char Saint-Chamond, as it was known, was undertaken by Colonel Rimailho of F.A.M.H who took as starting-point a lengthened Holt Caterpillar chassis, which had been specially built up from parts of three Holt tractors for comparison with the Schneider-built chassis in trials at Vincennes on 21 February 1916.

The prototype vehicle of Saint-Chamond design was completed by September 1916, and it was in its essentials a larger version of the Schneider; but although the tracks were longer the much larger hull led to a considerable overhang at front and rear which, it was soon found, resulted in poor cross-country performance and handling characteristics. It is interesting to note that the original designs included a third single wide track at the front, which should have considerably improved the climbing ability of the machine, although it would also have accentuated its nose-heaviness. Probably for the latter reason and also, doubtless, to simplify production, this feature was not included in the tanks built.

In addition to the handling faults, the Saint-Chamond was found to have further defects when in action for the first time on 5 May 1917. Facilities for crew exit in emergency were poor, vision arrangements were inadequate and the recoil cylinder of the 75-mm. gun was found to be vulnerable to enemy fire.

The Saint-Chamond had an electric transmission—a Panhard four-cylinder petrol engine of 80–90-h.p. operated a 52-kw dynamo which in turn supplied two electric motors, one to each track. This system eliminated the gear changing difficulties inherent in other early tanks and simplified steering (for which controls were provided at either end of the vehicle) but it was complicated and delicate and, unfortunately, unreliable and added to all the other troubles with this tank.

In an effort to correct at least some of these faults, modifications were introduced both in the course of production and retrospectively. After the first 165 tanks (of the 400 ordered) were built, the 75-mm. Saint-Chamond T.R. gun was replaced by the standard 75-mm. Model 1897 field gun. The flat roof with two circular cupolas of the early tanks was modified to a new pattern higher at the front to give more headroom to the crew—there was one square cupola at the left on most tanks. The tracks, which were too narrow, were replaced with wider ones with a chevron tread pattern to give more traction and to accommodate these the hull side plates over the tracks had to be modified.

It was recommended that additional $8\frac{1}{2}$-mm. plates should be added to the side plates (which were a basic $8\frac{1}{2}$ mm.) to give full protection against the German 'K' bullet, although this modification was not carried out in full.

Other features of the Char Saint-Chamond were the four Hotchkiss machine-guns (one each side, one at the front, one at the back with 8488 rounds carried) in addition to the main weapon (for which 106 rounds were supplied) mounted in the front plate; its crew of nine men, and its weight (due mainly to its heavy transmission system) of 24 tons.

None of the modifications introduced could make the Saint-Chamond into a good tank and, after the French had given consideration to other designs to replace it and the Schneider C.A., it was decided to accept the offer of British heavy tanks for employment in the offensive planned for 1919.

64 Armoured Car, Pierce-Arrow (3-pdr.), 1916, U.K.

The Pierce-Arrow heavy armoured cars with 3-pdr. gun used in Russia in 1916–17 by the British Naval armoured car force led by Commander Oliver Locker-Lampson were successors to the Seabrook 3-pdr. cars of the R.N.A.S. Armoured Car Division. In place of the open 3-pdr. mounting of the Seabrook the Pierce-Arrow was fitted with a rotating, fully enclosed turret, just forward of the rear wheels. The driver's cab was only half the width of the body and was the only interruption to all-round traverse of the gun. The driver's vision port was protected by a 3-in. thick Triplex bullet-proof glass block, which was replaceable. Behind the turret, and with side plates only, was an open compartment for the carriage of stores or men. The armour plate thickness varied between the batches built—in 1917 5-mm. plate was used, although

the earlier cars had $\frac{3}{4}$-in. or 9-mm. plate.

The origin of this design is uncertain but it seems that a prototype may have been constructed for Locker-Lampson by a French shipyard at Dunkirk in 1915. Two, and probably others, of the cars sent to Russia in 1916–17 were, however, armoured by W. G. Allen & Sons at Tipton, Staffordshire, although the turntables for the 3-pdrs. were made by John Shearman & Co.'s shipyard at Newport, Monmouthshire.

Records seem to indicate that five Pierce-Arrow armoured cars were with Locker-Lampson's expedition in Russia and another chassis was sent out from the U.K. without armour, possibly with the intention that armour should be fitted after arrival. One was lost in action during the fighting and the last car was not sent until September 1917, probably as a replacement. Two of the cars were originally 'pom-pom'-equipped vehicles belonging to the Royal Marine Artillery A.A. Brigade and were among the batch of armoured cars surplus to requirements which had been handed over to the R.N.A.S. Armoured Car Division about August 1915. One of these two retained its original armament in Russia at first, although this was apparently changed later on. It is more than probable that, in fact, all of Locker-Lampson's 3-pdr. Pierce-Arrows (with the possible exception of the last) were converted R.M.A. vehicles. The engine armour was identical in both the 'pom-pom' and the 3-pdr. cars.

Although the Pierce-Arrows were used widely in the actions in which the British armoured car force in Russia took part, they were not always popular because their loaded weight of over

9 tons not infrequently caused them to get bogged down, and they were also criticized as being of top-heavy design. In one car, at least, the weight was reduced by the turret being removed and replaced by a 3-pdr. on an open mounting with a flat shield. The gaps in the sides left by removal of the turret were filled in with flat steel plates.

65 Packard Armoured Car, 1916, Russia.

The Vickers quick-firing 40-mm. automatic gun was mounted in a turret with a wide arc of fire to make the most of its potentialities in the Russian Packard heavy armoured car of 1916.

The history of this vehicle is not clear but it appears to have been armoured in England by the Wolseley subsidiary of Vickers Ltd. during 1915 and delivered by the following year. The chassis was an American-built 3-ton lorry type with a 13-ft wheelbase and 32·4-h.p. engine. The final drive was by chains to the rear wheels. The tyres were solid rubber, twin at the rear.

The car (only one seems to have been built) appears to have been modified in Russia: the wheel discs were removed (perhaps in an attempt to cut down unnecessary weight) although the rear body armour was raised in height. One of the drawings shows it in this form.

66 King Armoured Car and White Armoured Car, 1916–17, U.S.A.

The King Motor Car Co. of Detroit and The White Motor Co. of Cleveland, Ohio both supplied chassis for armoured cars in 1916–17 to the United States Ordnance Department.

The earlier of the two types, the King, designed by Captain W. A. Ross and constructed by the Armored Motor Car Co. of Detroit, was rather reminiscent of the British Royal Naval Air Service turreted armoured cars—the resemblance heightened by the use of a turret with bevelled edges. The King was fairly small for an armoured car, however. Wire spoke wheels—dual at the rear—were fitted, and equipped with pneumatic tyres. The King had an eight-cylinder engine, was protected by $\frac{1}{4}$-in. plate, had a crew of three and weighed just over $2\frac{1}{2}$ (short) tons. Two 12-in. wide wooden unditching planks (steel trussed) could be carried on brackets each side. This car, and later, slightly different versions, were tested by the U.S. Marine Corps.

The White shown in the drawings was built in 1917 and was generally similar to the King layout but had disc wheels fitted with solid rubber tyres and a straightforward cylindrical turret with a flat top.

There was an earlier version with a higher hull which was used in 1916 on the Mexican border, but the 1917 model was purely experimental.

67 Gun Carrier, Mark I, 1917, U.K.

The Gun Carrier was suggested as a companion machine to Tank, Mark I to carry forward medium artillery and ammunition over shell-torn ground covered with old and new trench systems. It was apparent by mid-1916 that offensives on both sides (and notably the German attack at Verdun in February–July 1916) soon lost their drive through the difficulty of bringing up artillery to maintain support.

The idea of a gun-carrying tank was

put forward by Major Gregg of the Metropolitan Carriage, Wagon and Finance Co., who were the builders of the greater proportion of Tanks Mark I produced. Design commenced in July 1916 and the prototype, built by the Metropolitan Carriage, Wagon and Finance Co., was running at the beginning of 1917.

The Gun Carrier, Mark I, as it became designated, used the main mechanical components of Tank, Mark I, including the steering tail wheels (which were later discarded). The purpose for which the Gun Carrier was designed, however, necessitated a changed arrangement and resulted in an entirely different appearance from the tank. The layout comprised an open space at the front in to which the artillery piece (usually a 60-pdr. gun or a 6-in. howitzer) could be winched up a ramp, and behind this space an armoured box which contained a crew compartment and the engine and transmission. In the prototype, the driver and brakesman sat in the open over either track in front of the rear compartment, but in production machines two armoured cabs, either side of the breach of the gun, were fitted. This layout required the engine (a 105-h.p. Daimler) to be placed at the rear (unlike the Tank Mark I) with transmission shaft leading forwards to the differential which was located near the front of the armoured compartment. The final drive chains then led back to drive sprockets at the rear of the track assembly. Overall tracks, as in the heavy tanks, were not provided for in the Gun Carrier and the fact that the tracks went through tunnels under the front crew cabs and the rear compartment led to difficulties with mud collecting at these points.

Forty-eight Gun Carriers were built (two similar machines were completed as Salvage Tanks), the majority of them by Kitson & Co. at Leeds, by July 1917. In France, they were used far less for carrying artillery than ammunition. The vehicle was designed so that the 60-pdr. gun or the 6-in. howitzer could be fired from it, although from a practical point of view only the 6-in. howitzer could be used in this way. These weapons were employed in this fashion at night on a few occasions and achieved some tactical success, but the Gun Carrier companies were eventually converted into supply companies and carried other supplies as well as ammunition. When transporting a medium gun or howitzer, sixty-four rounds of ammunition could be carried or, without the weapon 130 rounds, or approximately seven tons of supplies. It was estimated that six Gun Carriers with their combined crews of twenty-four men could carry a load which would otherwise require 1745 men—the only practicable alternative form of cross-country transport.

68 Armoured Car, Ford (Admiralty pattern), 1917, U.K.

The Ford was designed as an ultra-light armoured car to complement the Pierce-Arrow heavy armoured cars and the Lanchester 'light' armoured cars with the Royal Naval Armoured Car force in Russia. By 1916 the Ford's rugged reputation and ability to go almost anywhere in civilian use had been reinforced by outstanding service with Light Car Patrols in the Middle

East. Ford light wagons and cars had also been supplied in some numbers to the Admiralty and so this chassis was an obvious choice for a light armoured car. The Ford Model T itself needs little description—the 22-h.p. four-cylinder side-valve engine with two speeds and planetary transmission remained virtually unchanged for years, as did the essentials of the chassis, with its spidery transverse front suspension.

The design of the armoured car was undertaken at the Newport, Monmouthshire, base in the United Kingdom of the Russian armoured car force by Chief Petty Officer L. Gutteridge. Basically it consisted of an armoured, open-top body at the back, an armoured cab for the driver, and protection for the engine.

The work on the chassis to receive the armour included the addition of tie rods to strengthen the back axle, strengthening the front springs and fitting new, stronger rear springs. The armour—5-mm. plate—was bolted on to an angle-iron framework which was attached to the chassis to receive it. The armament was one Maxim water-cooled machine-gun (with a flat 9-mm. shield attached to the barrel) on a tripod which, with special sliding feet, was clamped to the floor of the body. A quick release device enabled the gun to be removed easily for use outside the vehicle.

Other equipment for the Ford armoured car included a special 10-gallon petrol tank; a carrier for a Stepney wheel (a spare wheel which could be attached to the outside of the normal rim as a 'get you home' device) and wheel discs. These last were used on the prototype—and disguised its distinc-

tive Ford appearance to some extent—but were omitted on the other cars built. The all up weight complete was 21 cwt., of which the armour represented 11 cwt.

The work of fitting the armour was carried out by W. G. Allen & Sons, Tipton, Staffordshire, although the finishing touches to the cars, including painting, were carried out by the R.N.A.S. at Newport. Nine Fords were armoured in this way during 1916, although it appears that not all were actually sent to Russia. Six cars, at any rate, reached the British force by December and were dispatched with a detachment to the Roumanian front. Although—like Fords generally—they were regarded somewhat humorously, the Ford armoured cars nevertheless gave a good account of themselves and certainly managed to stay more mobile than the heavier vehicles.

Not long before the Revolution in Russia in 1917, Chief Petty Officer Gutteridge, who by then had joined the Russian base of the R.N.A.S. at Kursk, designed a modified Ford armoured car with a shortened body to carry a Lewis gun and be operated by a crew of two men only. The car was altered and the casting for the Lewis gun mounting made, although the outbreak of Revolution made it impossible to finish the project. As the result of combat and a lack of spares the Naval armoured car unit was suffering a severe shortage of vehicles by the middle of 1917 and the armour from a wrecked Ford armoured car was fitted, disguised, round the body of a Fiat lorry and this improvised armoured car was used in action in support of the Russian 2nd Cavalry Division.

69 **Bremer Marien-Wagen Über-panzert (Voll Ketten),** 1917, Germany.

The Marien-Wagen, designed by H. Bremer and produced in the Daimler factory at Berlin-Marienfelde, was a cross-country lorry which appeared in several forms, some semi-tracked, others full-tracked, although the basis of them all was the Daimler four-ton lorry.

One of the fully tracked models was turned into an armoured vehicle by Josef Vollmer by the substitution of an armoured hull in place of the normal lorry cab and body and armouring the engine. This created what could be regarded as the first German tank, since it was completed by the early Spring of 1917. It was, in fact, closer in concept to an armoured personnel carrier: it had no fixed armament, although ports were provided for the use of the crew's weapons.

The lorry transmission in the Marien-Wagen was adapted to drive the rear pair of tracks, which were of rudimentary design, sprung on semi-elliptic leaf springs. The front pair of tracks were also sprung on semi-elliptics—they were used for steering and were not driven.

The armoured full-track Marien-Wagen was demonstrated to Von Hindenburg, Ludendorff and members of the General Staff on 11 March 1917. The generals were not impressed by the demonstration and were subsequently somewhat prejudiced against later attempts to produce a German tank.

Later on, a semi-tracked version of the Marien-Wagen, in which a much more satisfactory type of rear track had been developed, was fitted with the armoured hull and turret of an Ehrhardt armoured car. This was only an experimental vehicle, but is interesting in foreshadowing the extensive development by the Germans of armoured half-tracks in the Second World War.

70 **Panzerkraftwagen Ehrhardt/17,** 1917, Germany.

When it was decided to form further German armoured car units a production order for new cars was given to the Ehrhardt firm alone because both Daimler and Büssing were fully engaged with other war work.

The first twelve Ehrhardt armoured cars built in 1917 were used to create 'Panzer Kraftwagen MG Züge 2, 3, 4, 5 and 6'—smaller units than the first experimental one, each equipped with two armoured cars and supporting transport. Twenty more Ehrhardt armoured cars were ordered later in 1917.

These new cars were very similar to the 1915 prototype but incorporated some of the lessons learned from operational use of all three makes of experimental vehicle. Most important was that the weight was reduced by nearly $1\frac{3}{4}$ tons. Underneath protection was added; provision was made for the turret to rotate instead of being fixed; and the vision ports were better protected. The radiator armour was revised, with horizontal grilles similar to those of the Daimler 1915 model, adjusted by a lever from the driver's seat, and the headlamps were enclosed in armoured boxes. The rear wheels also were enclosed. Wireless equipment with a tall extensible aerial was included. This apparatus, which could only be used when the car was stationary, was generally unpopular with the crews because it took up valuable space inside. Although large cars, the interior was rather cramped when carrying the normal crew of 8–9 men.

Some of the cars were used with success on the Ukranian front in 1918.

After the war, with internal unrest and danger on the Eastern frontiers, twenty more cars of this type were constructed in Germany in 1919. These were almost identical to the 1917 model, with only minor external changes, but the run-down German steel industry could only provide armour of poor quality which offered inferior protection.

71 **Char Renault FT 17**, 1917, France.

First ordered in 1916 only as a command vehicle to operate with the heavy Schneider and Saint-Chamond tanks, the Renault light tank by the summer of 1918 represented the principal French effort in armoured fighting vehicle production and a battalion of Renault tanks per week (75) was being delivered by August 1918.

Louis Renault was first asked in late 1915 to undertake tank production but at this time declined to do so, because his factory was already fully occupied with work on producing other armaments and had had no experience of tracked vehicles.

When asked again, in July 1916, to design and produce a tank—a light type to specialize in infantry support— Renault this time accepted and immediately put his meteoric enthusiasm and energy into the project. Renault closely supervised the design and himself drove the prototype tank for the first time when it was ready for trials on 22 February 1917.

There had been considerable indecision in official circles during the preceding eight months, but by this time a firm order for 150 Renault tanks was placed; the intention being at this stage that the light tanks should be used as command tanks with the heavy battalions. Indecision prevailed, however, and the order was suspended because of difficulties over the design of the turret. In May the production order was reinstated and greatly increased by 1000 to a total of 1150 and later—in the Autumn—by a further 2500. The order now comprised tanks equipped with a 37-mm. cannon and signal tanks, as well as the original machine-gun-armed vehicles.

The new order was beyond even the resources of the Renault concern alone and production was then allocated as 1850 tanks to be produced by the parent company, 800 by Berliet, 600 by Schneider (subcontracted to SOMUA) and 280 by Delaunay-Belleville. The decision to include other manufacturers was inevitable, but led to difficulties over interchangeability of spare parts later on because, with French individualism, the other firms used their own methods in manufacture rather than accept Renault's standards in detail. The armour plate for Renault tanks was supplied from the United Kingdom (The Miris Steel Company, Sheffield, was the main contractor) and at first the quality was unsatisfactory and delivery dates were uncertain.

The Renault tank included successfully for the first time many of the features which came to be adopted in many post First World War tanks and the general layout is still widely used today. The hull consisted of an armour box, without chassis, with the driver at the front, the gunner behind him and the engine at the rear.

The engine used was an adaptation of the Renault 18-h.p. touring car model, the four-cylinder 95/160, which developed 35 b.h.p. The use of a standard engine which was already in mass production greatly simplified the construction of large numbers of tanks. Transmission to the tracks was via rear sprockets; track suspension was achieved by leaf springs carrying the whole track frames. Steering was by the clutch and brake method.

The Renault was the first tank to go into mass production with a revolving turret and difficulties over this feature caused delays in production. Mounted on a ball race it was of rounded cast construction in the prototype, but replaced by an octagonal built-up structure in the first 100 production vehicles. Later production tanks had improved versions of rounded and multi-sided turrets. The first vehicles had an 8-mm. Hotchkiss air-cooled machine-gun, but when the 37 mm. Purteaux cannon had been modified to semi-automatic operation so that it could be fired by one man a proportion of the later tanks were equipped with this weapon. In fact, in February 1918 the production orders were for 1000 machine-gun-armed tanks and 1830 with the 37-mm. gun; signal tanks and self-propelled 75-mm. gun mountings on Renault chassis forming the balance.

The Renault tanks were used in action on 31 May 1918, for the first time, not in large numbers as the French had always hoped, but to help stem the German offensive. Nevertheless, their mobility surprised the enemy. During the Allied offensives between June and November they were used in increasing numbers and twenty-seven battalions were equipped with them at the time of the Armistice.

After the war the Renault continued in use with the French Army for many years and into the Second World War, and was also adopted by many other countries, in its original form and in foreign-built developments.

72 **Austin-Putilov Half-Tracked Armoured Car**, 1917, Russia.

The half-tracked vehicle, in which the rear wheels are replaced by tracks, was developed in the early days mainly in the U.S.A., where several petrol-engined commercial types were produced and used between 1900 and 1914. The half-track as an armoured car was, however, first developed in Russia.

An experimental type was built about 1915 on a Lombard tractor (numbers of which had been supplied in quantity by the U.S.A.) and known as the Gulkevitch armoured car. This had steel front wheels, with wire spokes. Another, larger, vehicle also with a turret (although cylindrical with a flat top unlike the bevelled roof turret of the Gulkevitch) had disc-type front wheels with solid rubber tyres.

Much more successful than these were the vehicles designed by Adolphe Kégresse who was the technical manager of the Tsar's garage in Petrograd. These had their origin in the system evolved to improve traction in snow, where light rubber tracks were first fitted in 1910 to replace the rear wheels on some of the Tsar's motor cars. In 1917 the Kégresse system was applied to Austin armoured cars and vehicles of both the original British type and the Austin-Putilov type were converted to half-tracks.

In the conversion, the rear wheels were removed and replaced by Kégresse's tracks which consisted of, each side, a front idler wheel, four small double road wheels, sprung in pairs and a rear driving wheel. The rubber track with a ribbed pattern to increase adhesion was a continuous band. Transmission was taken from pinions on the end of the original axles (which were in the centre of the track assembly) by Coventry chains to sprockets on the extensions of the rear driving wheels. Drive to the track itself was transmitted by friction only. Each track unit was pivoted about the driving axle, permitting an upward or downward movement of over 11 in. either end.

The artillery type front wheels with pneumatic tyres of the normal armoured cars were replaced in the half-track model by disc wheels with flanges on either side of the rubber tyres. An interesting method of preventing ditching or 'bellying' (the vehicle grounding on its chassis between the front wheels and the tracks) was adopted in the Austin-Putilov version (although it does not appear to have been used in the Austin model). This consisted of two pivoted sprung arms projecting in front of the car, each carrying a roller. A shorter arm of the same sort also projected in front of and behind each track.

The Kégresse device was very successful and for Russian conditions a great advance over ordinary wheeled vehicles and 300 sets were ordered—sixty of these were intended for use on Austin or Austin-Putilov armoured cars. After the Revolution the greater part of this order remained uncompleted but a few were built by Kégresse himself before he left Russia and, it is believed, some more under the Soviet Government. Some of these half-track armoured cars were used in 1920 against the Poles, who captured a few of them.

73   Tank, Mark IV, 1917, U.K.

On 19 September 1916—four days after the first tanks went into action— the British Commander-in-Chief, Sir Douglas Haig, gave an order for 1000 further tanks to be constructed immediately. (This order was rescinded three weeks later by the Army Council, but immediately reinstated by Mr Lloyd George, Secretary of State for War, who had more foresight). Several faults had revealed themselves in the Tank, Mark I and it was desired to improve the design to eliminate some of these before going into mass production of the 100 new tanks. A small bridging order for 100 tanks of the original type, in which some improvements could be introduced during the course of production, was sanctioned by Lloyd George. This order would ensure that the factories, which were then still completing the last of the Mark Is, would be kept going until the new standard pattern was settled.

The interim vehicles, designated

Tanks, Mark II and III—fifty of each—were delivered between about January and March 1917. It was understood that these 100 tanks would be used only for training purposes and soft plates were used in their construction instead of armour plate and this was the cause of unfair criticism of the Mechanical Warfare Supply Department when some of these tanks were hurriedly gathered together for use in action in March.

The first of the tanks of the new design, Mark IV (again principally the work of Major W. G. Wilson in conjunction with Tritton of William Foster & Co.) were delivered to the Army towards the end of April 1917. Although superficially very much the same in appearance as the Mark Is and the same engine and transmission system was used, they did, in fact, incorporate many changes suggested by battle experience. The armour protection was improved—although the maximum thickness of 12 mm. was the same, the use of plates of this dimension was extended. The armament in the Male tanks was changed from the long 6-pdrs. (40 calibre), which were liable to damage when the tank ditched, to short 6-pdr. guns, 23 calibres long. These were mounted in modified sponsons which could (in both Male and Female version) be swung inwards for rail transport—on the Mark I the sponsons had to be unbolted—a time-consuming and heavy task. Another armament change, although requested by the Army, turned out to be a retrograde step. This was the introduction of the Lewis machine-gun in both Male and Female tanks. This weapon had given good and reliable service with the infantry but turned out to be unsuccessful when used in tanks because the cooling jacket could not be protected and was very vulnerable to small arms fire, and the Lewis's cooling system sucked dust into the gunner's eyes. The mounting was more liable to penetration than that of the Hotchkiss and in some tanks a Hotchkiss was substituted for the Lewis in the front plate between the driver and commander. In later tanks the Hotchkiss (in a modified form with belt feed and pistol grip) was re-introduced in place of all the Lewis guns.

The crew conditions were improved by the introduction of better emergency escape hatches, better vision arrangements and a more effective cooling and ventilation system.

The petrol supply for the engine was now by means of a vacuum feed system, which obviated the disadvantage in the Mark I's gravity feed, which frequently ceased to work when the tank was ditched. The petrol was carried in an armoured container at the rear outside the main hull in the Mark IV where it was less of a fire risk. The exhaust system was fitted with a silencer—which was absent in the earlier tanks. Steering tail wheels were not used in Mark IV—they had been dropped in Marks II–III and were also removed eventually from Mark Is.

The 105-b.h.p. Daimler engine was continued in use for the Mark IV to simplify production, although it was realized that the tank was underpowered. An uprated version, speeded up from 1000 r.p.m to 1250 r.p.m. and giving 125 b.h.p. was introduced and was used for the later Mark IVs. It was found unreliable in the hands of the troops, however, and for this reason the tanks fitted with this type of engine were among those selected for conversion to tank tenders—supply-carrying tanks.

To overcome the problem of the tank ditching, 'torpedo spuds' were devised—a cylindrical beam attached to each track, which gave the track a better purchase on the ground and helped it to pull the tank out of the hole. This was only partly successful and was replaced by a single wide beam attached to both tracks by chains. Twin rails over the top of the hull carried the beam clear of the driver's cab. This device worked well and was continued in subsequent patterns of wartime heavy tanks.

The order for Mark IVs—the 1000 was just exceeded—was made up of 595 Female and 420 Male tanks. The prototype and approximately one third of the production machines were built by William Foster & Co., and the rest by the Metropolitan Carriage Wagon & Finance Co. Some of the Females were later converted into 'Hermaphrodites' by having the right machine-gun sponson exchanged for a Male 6-pdr. sponson. This was to give them a weapon to use against enemy tanks, following the first engagement with German tanks in April 1918.

Mark IVs were first used in action in June 1917 and by November formed the greater part of the strength of the Tank Corps at the battle of Cambrai—commemorated as the first really successful battle for the tanks. Some continued in use until the end of the war, although by then later models with better mechanical performance and trench-crossing ability had been produced. As an experiment in trench crossing, however, a Mark IV was fitted with a 'Tadpole Tail'—a mild steel extension of the rear horns which increased the span which could be traversed from 10 ft to about 14 ft. This device lacked rigidity, however, and was dropped in favour of extending the main hull of the tank, as was done in the Mark V*. A 'Tadpole Tail', Mark IV was later fitted with a 6-in. trench mortar between the rear horns to experiment with close support for tanks in the attack.

74 Leichter Kampfwagen I, 1917, Germany.

Many powerful passenger cars were laid up in Germany by 1917 because neither petrol nor tyres were available to keep them running. The attractive idea was conceived of turning these into light tanks by using the existing engine and chassis and adding track frames and tracks and building up an armoured hull in place of the motor car body.

Josef Vollmer, a leading German military automotive engineer, was instructed to produce a design and the L.K.I.-Leichter Kampfwagen, Modell I—was the first experimental type to appear. The motor car layout was altered as little as possible, so the engine was at the front with the fighting compartment at the rear. The conventional motor car transmission necessitated the drive sprockets being at the back. Steering was by differential braking—perhaps the first use of this system for a tracked vehicle. Trench-crossing considerations no doubt demanded the rather disproportionate length of 18 ft (the track frames were extended well in front of the car chassis)—width was 6 ft 7 in. and height 8 ft 2 in. and weight just under 7 tons. The maximum armour protection was 8 mm. and the armament carried in the small revolving turret was one water-cooled machine-gun, with another, unmounted, in reserve. A version of the L.K. I with a 3·7-cm. gun was planned but was never built because demonstration of the prototypes led the Kriegsministerium to issue a new specification for a light tank which necessitated a complete redesign.

75 Tank, Medium, Mark A, 1917, U.K.

A military requirement for a lighter and faster machine than the then standard Tank, Mark I was formulated towards the end of 1916. It was envisaged that such a machine should be able to exploit a breakthrough of the enemy defences by the heavy tanks and co-operate with the cavalry. For this role the great length of the standard heavy tanks needed to facilitate trench crossing was not quite so important, so lightness could be achieved by a reduction in size and also, it was at first decided, by a decrease in armour thickness.

Sir William Tritton of William Foster & Co. Ltd. of Lincoln undertook the design and manufacture of a prototype vehicle to meet these requirements and this, known as 'Tritton's Light Machine' or 'Tritton Chaser', was completed in early February 1917.

The more compact dimensions of 'Tritton's Light Machine' led him to place the crew behind the power plant which was, however, in roughly the same relative position in the vehicle as in the heavy tanks, with drive to the rear track sprockets. In order to achieve sufficient power with engines which

were available for tank use and at the same time avoid the cumbersome gear change and steering arrangements of the heavies, twin Tylor commercial vehicle engines, each complete with its own clutch and gear-box, were used. The two systems were joined at the cross-shaft from whence final drive to the tracks was by chains to sprockets on either side. For steering the clutches joining the cross-shaft were released and one or the other engine speeded up, the turn being on the side opposite to that of the faster running engine. The steering effect could be increased by use of the brakes on one engine or another. This arrangement had the advantage of being controlled by one man only but it called for a great deal of skill on the part of the driver, because one or both of the engines could be stalled if care was not exercised. To aid performance by decreasing track friction, rollers to carry the top run of the track and a series of chutes along the sides to clear mud were introduced.

The armament consisted of one Lewis machine-gun—then temporarily in favour for tanks—mounted in a revolving turret of the pattern used in Austin armoured cars. The turret was off-set on the left-hand side of the hull (the driver's cab was lower and on the right) and had all-round traverse and a commanding field of fire—the gun mounting was approximately 9 ft above ground level.

A production order was given for 200 vehicles based on 'Tritton's Light Machine' and designated Tanks, Medium Mark A. Several changes were made in the production machines, the most prominent being the replacement of the revolving turret by a fixed structure with four ball mountings for Hotchkiss machine-guns. This change was made to simplify production. The armour thickness was increased from the 9-mm. maximum of Tritton's prototype to the 14-mm. standard of the heavy tanks. The petrol tank, which was unarmoured in the original model, was moved from between the rear horns to the front, where it was enclosed in an armoured box. There were also other minor adjustments at other points including the exhaust system and elimination of the rear mud chutes on each side, which were replaced by round inspection plates. All these changes increased the weight of the Medium Mark A to 14 tons, compared with approximately 12 tons for the 'Tritton Chaser', although performance does not appear to have been greatly affected.

The first Medium Mark As were built in October 1917 and they were being delivered in quantity to the Tank Corps in the field by March 1918. They first went into action on 26 March to help stem the German offensive when twelve 'Whippets' (as the Medium became widely known) near Colincamps surprised and put to flight two infantry battalions.

An order for a further 185 Medium Mark As was subsequently commuted to one for Mark Bs, which promised to be a better design. Experimental modifications by the Tank Corps Central Workshops in France to a Mark A included the addition of leaf springs to the suspension and later the substitution of a Rolls-Royce 360-h.p. aero engine for the Tylor engines. These changes increased the speed of the tank from about 8 m.p.h. to no less than 30 m.p.h.

76 Schwerer Kampfwagen A7V, 1917, Germany.

Several designs for cross-country armoured 'landships'—both tracked and wheeled—were submitted to the German High Command both before the war and right up to the time the first British tanks went into action on 15 September 1916. The moral effect of this attack was out of all proportion to its tactical success, which was small, and led German Army commanders on the Western Front to press for a German equivalent. The High Command had already had some inkling of what was going on in England but now took action for the first time to promote the development of a German landship by appointing a committee composed of engineering experts from leading heavy engineering and automotive firms to study this question. The committee was known for security purposes as 'Allegemeine Kriegsdepartement 7, Abteilung Verkehrswesen' or 'General War Department 7, Traffic Section'.

A general specification was laid down and as a first step towards design the committee obtained a Holt tractor from Austria: this American-designed caterpillar tractor (built under licence in Budapest) was at that time the only suitable tracklaying vehicle available to Germany for experiment. It is interesting to note here that the Holt had also inspired Colonel Swinton's landship proposals put before the War Office in Britain and also formed the basis for the French heavy tanks.

After trials of the Holt tractor, a lengthened version of the chassis was designed by Josef Vollmer, powered by two Daimler engines of 100 h.p. each (the original proposals for one 80–100-h.p. engine being recognized as inadequate) and, fitted with a wooden mock-up of an armoured hull, was first demonstrated in the Spring of 1917. There were some changes in the original requirements laid down for armour and armament because the protection was intended to be 30-mm. thickness overall, but this was later altered, to reduce total weight, to 30 mm. at the front only, the remainder varying between 15 mm. and 20 mm. For the main armament, different guns were tested and the choice eventually fell on the 5·7-cm. Sokol, a captured Russian weapon, of which a small supply was available. However, only one gun was fitted (at the front) instead of the original intention of having a shell-firing weapon at both ends. In addition six water-cooled machine-guns (MG '08) were carried—two on each side and two at the rear.

The design was accepted and the tank (known as A7V from a contraction of the design committee's title) was put into series production, the contracts having already been awarded. One hundred vehicles were ordered, of which only twenty were finally completed as tanks, the first of these being ready in October 1917.

The first action in which the A7Vs took part was at St Quentin on 21 March 1918; the first tank versus tank action on 24 April. This encounter showed one fundamental advantage of the German tanks in that all were equipped with a gun, the British Tanks Mark IV, Female version, equipped with machine-guns only, being helpless against the 5·7-cm. gun of the A7V. The central placing of the A7V's main gun was also a better feature than the sponson mountings of the British tanks. The design of the A7V was better than that of the British vehicles in some of the details—sprung tracks for example—and in some of the wider conceptions, such as thicker armour and a higher power/weight ratio. Overall, however, the A7V was far less successful as a battle vehicle. The most serious fault was in cross-country performance and trench-crossing ability which were poor because of the high centre of gravity and low tracks with the hull overhanging at front and rear. The Sokol guns had a lower rate of fire than the British 6-pdrs. Early tanks had mechanical faults and the armour plate was badly fitted and in some cases of inferior quality. These faults were corrected later (some tanks had single large side plates instead of several sections, for example) but the basic design could not be altered. The Germans made as much use as possible of captured tanks and the A7V's successor was modelled on the layout of the British machines.

77 Char Renault TSF, 1917, France.

The Renault signal tank or Char TSF (télégraphie sans fil) was called for by General Estienne when the big order for 2500 Renaults was placed in the Autumn of 1917. It was intended as a command vehicle to provide contact between units and with their headquarters or supporting arms or as an observation vehicle.

The number of signal tanks required was originally 200 but this was later increased in early 1918 to 470.

All the mechanical details of the Char TSF were the same as those of the

Renault gun-tanks. In the signal vehicle the crew was increased from two to three men—driver, radio operator and observer/commander and the turret was replaced by a fixed armoured superstructure, equipped with a cupola on top, an observation window in front and a periscope, and housed the radio set. In the prototype vehicles the superstructure overhung the hull sides but in production tanks—as shown in the drawings—this was changed so that the hull itself did not have to be modified.

78 Holt Gas-Electric Tank, 1918, U.S.A.

The first tank designed and built in the United States—as opposed to the various mock-ups and models which preceded it—the Holt Gas-Electric Tank was the product of co-operation between the Holt Manufacturing Company and the General Electric Company.

The vehicle, which was built during 1917 and completed early in 1918, consisted of a simple armoured box hull on a lengthened and modified version (with pivoted track frames) of the Caterpillar suspension used for the Holt tractors employed extensively in the War for gun hauling. The engine was a Holt four-cylinder petrol type with forced water cooling, developing 90 h.p. This operated a G.E.C. generator which provided the current to drive two electric motors, one motor for each track. The tank was steered by varying the current to either motor in conjunction with a brake on each motor shaft—for a turn the track was braked on the opposite side to the track driven.

The hull, which was armoured to a thickness between 6 and 15 mm., was V-shaped at the front where a 75-mm. mountain howitzer was mounted low down, just above the tracks. In addition there were several mountings—two of them in sponsons either side—for 0·30 in. machine-guns, although normally only two of these were carried. The crew consisted of six men.

The Holt tank was 16 ft 6 in. long, 9 ft 1 in. wide and 7 ft $9\frac{1}{2}$ in. high, but weighed 25 (short) tons because of the weight of the transmission and the maximum speed was only 6 m.p.h. Only a prototype was built.

79 Steam Tank (Tracked), 1918, U.S.A.

The Steam Tank of 1918 was specially built as a vehicle to carry into action a successful type of flame-thrower designed by an officer of the U.S. Army Engineer Corps. The supporters of this project were General John A. Johnson, backed somewhat improbably by the Endicott and Johnson Shoe Company and Phelan and Ratchesky, the Boston bankers.

The model for the general design for this tank was a British Tank, Mark IV which was then in the U.S.A., but steam engines were chosen as the motive power because the flame-thrower, around which the tank was to be built, was originally planned to be steam driven. The tank engines were twin two-cylinder steam units—one to each track—activated by two kerosene-burning boilers. The total output was 500 h.p. Weighing 50 (short) tons and being 34 ft 9 in. long and with rigid suspension, the maximum speed was 4 m.p.h.

The armour was to a maximum of

$\frac{1}{2}$-in. thickness and the armament consisted of four 0·30-in. machine-guns and, of course, the flame-thrower. This weapon, as finally built, used a 35-h.p. petrol engine to compress the oil flame fuel to a pressure of 1600 lbs. per square inch and project it, ignited, through a small nozzle. At a range of 90 yards this produced a ball of flame 20 ft in diameter which was intended to put concrete strongpoints out of action.

Completed in Boston, where it was first demonstrated in April 1918, the prototype (and only) Steam Tank (Tracked) was the second tank to be built in the U.S.A. It should not be confused with the later steam tank built by the Holt Manufacturing Co., which was a three-wheeled vehicle.

80 Armoured Car, Austin (1918 pattern), 1918, U.K.

The 17th (Armoured Car) Battalion, Tank Corps had the distinction of leading the British Army into Cologne on 6 December 1918 after the Armistice and of carrying the red, brown and green flag of the Tank Corps across the Rhine.

The equipment of the battalion consisted of Austin Armoured Cars of the pattern shown in the drawings. These were of the final type to be built on the Austin 30-h.p. 'Colonial' chassis during the First World War. All the earlier cars were built for, and delivered to, the Russian Imperial Government and supplies were terminated only when the Revolution occurred in November 1917. Although all the wartime Austins were of the same general appearance, there were successive improvements in the British-built cars (some chassis were

also armoured or modified in Russia, as shown elsewhere in this book) between 1914 and 1917 which finally resulted in the type adopted by the Tank Corps.

Light Armoured Motor Batteries were being formed for service in Persia in early 1918 and some of the Austin Armoured Cars diverted from the Russians were sent out to equip these. However, the German Spring offensive left no tanks available to equip the 17th Battalion Tank Corps which was in the process of formation in March 1918, so sixteen Austin Armoured Cars which were ready to be sent to the Middle East were handed over to the Tank Corps. The only change made in these cars was to replace the mountings for Vickers machine-guns with ball mountings to take the standard Tank Corps pattern Hotchkiss guns. In all, about 80 Austin Armoured Cars were supplied to the British Army.

Some other features of these cars were the dual rear wheels (the Russians preferred singles all round on their armoured cars), the Rubberine-filled tyres and the duplicate steering gear at the rear, although only the front wheels steered. Some of the earlier cars for Russia had dual steering, though only in the 1917–18 model was proper provision made in the armour design for a convenient rear driver's position. An interesting point about all Austin Armoured Cars was the stowage for spare wheels in the base of the turrets.

The Austin four-cylinder engine used in the armoured cars developed about 50 b.h.p. and gave the vehicle a top speed of 35 m.p.h. The armour consisted of 8-mm. plate on vertical surfaces, with 4 mm. on horizontal surfaces. Operated by a crew of five, the dimensions of the Austin Armoured Car (1918 type) were length 16 ft, width 6 ft 7 in., height 7 ft 10 in.

The Austin Armoured Cars performed useful work with the British Army in Mesopotamia and Persia as well as in France where the 17th Battalion Tank Corps achieved some outstanding feats behind the enemy lines in August 1918. However, the Austins were not nearly so robust as the R.N.A.S. Rolls-Royces and Lanchesters and their back axles were a constant source of weakness.

81 Tank, Mark V, 1918, U.K.

The worst fault in the early Tanks, Marks I–IV lay in the clumsy and inefficient driving system, which required the services of no less than four men— the driver, the tank commander (who acted as brakesman) and two other men, one on each side, who engaged the secondary gears for steering, on the instructions of the driver. Steering for turns of about 60 yards radius in good conditions could be managed by use of the tail wheels alone, but these were omitted after the Mark I because of failures in the mud of France. Otherwise, turns were made by the use of the brakes on one or the other side or the use of high or low gear on either side or by a combination of brakes and gears.

Even before the Mark IV was built, it was realized that a better form of transmission was necessary and experiments were put in hand to determine the best of alternative systems. The most likely of these were demonstrated at Oldbury on 3 March 1917—when the Mark IV was already in production —before a large audience of interested

parties. The competing transmission systems for the heavy tank shown were the Williams-Janney Hydraulic, Wilson Epicyclic, Daimler Petrol-Electric, Westinghouse Petrol-Electric and Wilkin's Multiple Clutch. All were linked with the Daimler six-cylinder engine; although in the case of the Daimler Petrol-Electric it had aluminium pistons, a lighter flywheel and ran at 1400 r.p.m. instead of 1000 r.p.m. The engine with the Westinghouse transmission ran at 1200 r.p.m.

All the systems could be operated by one man but Major Wilson's epicyclic was the most successful and it was adopted for Mark V, the heavy tank to follow Mark IV.

The Mark V was little changed in external aspect, but internally in addition to the new transmission it had a new engine specially designed for tank use by Mr H. Ricardo. This was a six-cylinder unit, developing 150 b.h.p. at 1250 r.p.m. It proved very reliable in service and was used for most of the other British tanks built during the war.

The increased power gave the Mark V a higher speed of 4·6 m.p.h. The average speed of the Mark V was, however, even greater than the average of the Marks I–IV because the difficulty of changing gear in the earlier tanks meant that often this was neglected and an inferior performance resulted.

Although performance was better and driving easier and the armour thickness increased to 14 mm. not all progress is upwards and the Mark V was less well ventilated than earlier tanks. The louvres on the hull sides near the rear are a feature which, together with the addition of a fixed conning tower in the centre of the hull, most readily distinguishes the Mark V from the Mark IV.

All Mark Vs used Hotchkiss machine-guns, but, otherwise the armament corresponded with that of Mark IV Male and Female respectively.

Four hundred Mark Vs—equally divided between Male and Female—were built during 1918 and the first time they were in action was in July of that year. To help Mark Vs tackle the wide trenches of the Hindenburg Line in the attack at the end of September 1918, 'cribs' were carried. This was a braced cylindrical framework which, dropped in the trench from the nose of the tank as a form of stepping stone, helped the machine to cross it. Cribs served the same purpose as the fascines (large bundles of chestnut palings) which had been used in the same fashion at Cambrai in 1917. However, whereas the fascine weighed 30 cwt. the crib weighed only 12 cwt. One of the drawings shows a crib being carried.

82 **Schwerer Kampfwagen A7V/U,** 1918, Germany.

The very inferior cross-country performance of the A7V was apparent at an early stage: the capture of British Mark IV tanks at Cambrai in November 1917 enabled the German engineers to examine the British machines in detail and better appreciate the good points of their design as well as their weaknesses. The great feature of the British tanks was their ability to move across shell-torn and entrenched ground —a feature owing much to the overall tracks and low centre of gravity helped by the armament being placed in side sponsons. The British machines were designed only for a short life and for ease of production, however, and lacked refinements and did not even have sprung tracks.

It was at first proposed that an exact copy of the British Tank, Mark IV should be put into production in Germany where drawings could have been made up from dimensions taken from captured vehicles. This suggestion was impracticable, first because of the difficulty in many cases of manufacturing identical components and, secondly, would have been wasteful of effort in that most if not all of the materials already in production for the A7V could not continue to be used.

The best solution for the A7V committee was to design a new tank on the lines of the British tanks, but utilizing as many of the original A7V components as possible. The result was known as A7V/U—the suffix denoting 'umlaufende Ketten', or overhead tracks. This tank, the prototype of which appeared in June 1918, was generally similar to the British tanks in appearance, although the side sponsons (each with one 5·7-cm. Sokol gun), necessitated by the use of overall tracks were placed rather further to the rear. The fact that the tracks were sprung and the relatively high power of the twin Daimler engines uprated to a total of 300 h.p. gave the A7V/U on trials a maximum speed of about $7\frac{1}{2}$ m.p.h.— around twice that of the British heavy tanks. Improvements over the A7V included increased armour protection and better ventilation.

The trials of the A7V/U showed that its heavier weight (nearly 40 tons) made it clumsy in action and limited its tactical employment and, furthermore, the track was liable to be shed by the design of the guide rails. These faults could be overcome, however, and twenty A7V/Us were ordered on 12 September 1918 although the end of the war put a stop to their production.

83 Skeleton Tank, 1918, U.S.A.

The aptly named Skeleton Tank built in the United States in 1918 was an experiment to achieve the maximum trench-crossing performance consistent with a weight of around 8 (short) tons.

Built by the Pioneer Tractor Company, of Winona, Minnesota, the Skeleton Tank included many structural members of ordinary iron pipe joined by standard plumbing connections.

The hull, which was a rectangular box armoured to a $\frac{1}{2}$-in. standard, was supported between the tracks and carried the driver at the front. The other crew member, the gunner, was behind him and operated the single 0·30-in. machine-gun mounted in a cylindrical turret. The engines (two Beaver four-cylinder water-cooled units, total h.p. 100) in the hull, drove sprockets at the rear of the track through a drive shaft to a differential carried in a separate small box between the rear horns of the tracks.

The Skeleton Tank could do a speed of between 2 and 5 m.p.h. cross-country; for its weight of only 8 tons it was 25 ft long and presumably satisfied the trench-crossing performance required of it, but with the end of the First World War, this ceased to be such an important characteristic and there was no further development of this interesting vehicle.

84 Tank, Mark VII, 1918, U.K.

The Williams-Janney hydraulic transmission which was tested in a Tank, Mark IV in March 1917, was introduced into a new tank destined for series production in 1918. This was the Mark VII, which externally was very much like its predecessor, the Mark V, although the hull length was extended by some 3 ft in order to improve the trench-crossing ability so important in heavy tanks of the era.

In the Mark VII the power from the engine (a 150-h.p. Ricardo, as in Mark V) was taken through reduction spur gears to two hydraulic variable speed gears and thence via independent cross shafts and chains to the track drive sprockets at the rear of the tank. The great advantage of this system was that the tank could be controlled by one man through two hand wheels, one for each variable speed gear unit. This resulted in a high degree of manoeuvrability and, through the infinite variety of ratios available, a good cross-country performance.

The prototype Tank, Mark VII was built by Brown Bros. of Edinburgh and completed in the second half of 1918. Large delays were encountered in production of the transmission units and no further Mark VIIs were produced by the time of the Armistice, when the production order was cancelled.

An earlier project, Tank, Mark VI, which had its main armament of one 6-pdr. gun mounted between the front horns, was also intended to use the Williams-Janney transmission, although this model reached only the mock-up stage and, unlike the Mark VII, not even a prototype was built.

85 Tank, Mark VIII, 1918, U.K./ U.S.A.

After the United States entered the war against Germany in April 1917, arrangements were put in hand so that the great manufacturing resources of the U.S.A. could be linked with British experience in tank design and operation to produce tanks in quantity for the use of both countries.

The 'Allied' or 'Liberty' tank or, more prosaically, Tank, Mark VIII was the result, although the intervention of the Armistice put an end to the plans for mass production.

A broad specification for the heavy tank likely to be needed for the battles on the Western Front in 1918–1919 was produced in France and given to an Anglo-American tank committee under the joint chairmanship of Lieut.-Col. Albert Stern (U.K.) and Major J. A. Drain (U.S.A.) and comprising Sir Eustace d'Eyncourt and Captain A. Green (a Tank Corps officer) as British members and Major H. W. Alden, U.S.A. Under the guidance of this committee, Lieutenant G. J. Rackham, then at the beginning of a distinguished career in A.F.V. and more general automotive engineering, produced the detailed drawings for the Mark VIII.

The new tank was recognizably an extension in design of earlier British tanks in layout and general appearance but it included many improvements suggested by earlier experience. The most fundamental of these was the complete separation of the engine compartment from the crew compartment by a bulkhead. This reduced the fire risk for the crew and furthermore the ventilating system kept the crew compartment at a slightly higher atmospheric pressure and so prevented fumes or heat from the engine entering.

The armour protection was increased —compared with earlier British tanks— to a 16-mm. maximum, although the armament, two 6-pdr. guns and seven machine-guns, was comparable. The trend of increasing length to meet ever wider trenches and tank obstacles was continued in the Mark VIII, which was 34 ft $2\frac{1}{2}$ in. long and could cross a gap of about 15 ft.

Although the Mark VIII at 37 tons was several tons heavier than previous tanks, performance was improved by the use of a 300-h.p. power unit and decrease in track ground pressure through the adoption of $26\frac{1}{2}$-in. wide tracks.

The engine intended for use in Mark VIIIs was the American 'Liberty' aero engine, with the alternative of a new 300-h.p. Ricardo, although an epicyclic transmission and steering system was employed in either case.

As mentioned, the Armistice put an end to the large-scale production plans for the Mark VIII, the first of which had been completed only just before fighting ceased. This was a hull shipped from England in July 1918 to the United States where a 'Liberty 'engine and the transmission were added. The first tank to be completed in Britain (where only seven in all were built—by the North British Locomotive Co. Ltd., Glasgow) —was at first fitted with a Rolls-Royce aero engine. All the later tanks (and subsequently the first one also) were powered by the 300-h.p. Ricardo twelve-cylinder engine, which was made up of two six-cylinder units.

In the United States it was decided

to complete 100 tanks and these were built during 1919 by the U.S. Ordnance Department. One of the American tanks is shown in the drawings. This differed externally from the British tanks in the armoured jackets for the Browning machine-guns used instead of the Hotchkiss guns used by the Tank Corps, and in other details, notably in the raised commander's/driver's superstructure.

86 Tank, Mark V*, 1918, U.K.

One of the obvious means of countering tank attacks was to increase the width of trenches. To meet this contingency, increasing length—and, hence, better trench-crossing ability—became a trend in the heavy tanks built towards the end of the war. The 'Tadpole Tail' tried on Tanks Mark IV and Mark V was not really successful and a much better alternative way of modifying standard tanks was worked out in February 1918 by the Central Workshops of the Tank Corps in France. This was, in effect, to cut a Mark V in half and insert three extra side panels behind the sponsons. This increased the length of the tank by 6 ft and its length overall to 32 ft 5in. The standard Mark V could cross a trench about 10 ft wide, but the modified type—designated Tank, Mark V*—could deal with a 14 ft trench.

The increased length of the Mark V* made for a more roomy hull and it was proposed to carry into the attack four spare machine-gun crews in tanks of this type, the idea being that the machine-gunners could be set down in forward positions to support the cavalry advance. Mark V*s were first used in

action in August 1918 at the Battle of Amiens and extra machine-gunners were taken up in the way proposed. The Mark V* had the imperfections of ventilation of the ordinary Mark V, however, and the unfortunate passengers, overcome by fumes and heat, were unfit to be of much immediate use when disembarked.

The Mark V* was mechanically the same as Mark V, apart from the extended transmission, so the increased length and weight (5 tons heavier) made for a more sluggish performance. The protection and armament were similar to that of the standard Mark Vs except that, in both Male and Female versions, an extra Hotchkiss machine-gun was introduced.

Six hundred and thirty-two Mark V*s were built, of which only 200 were Males, the main contractor—as for the Mark V—being the Metropolitan Carriage, Wagon & Finance Co. although the first few dozen seem to have been constructed, like the prototype, in France by the Tank Corps. They took part in most tank actions until the war's end. The American 301st Tank Battalion was partly equipped with them and served with the British Tank Corps.

87 Ford 3-ton Tank, 1918, U.S.A.

By the summer of 1918, the United States had embarked on a tank production programme based on the heavy Tank, Mark VIII, which was of British design, and a light tank which was an adaptation of the French Renault. In addition to these there was a requirement for an ultra-light vehicle to act as a machine-gun or ammunition carrier for the infantry.

As no suitable design for the infantry carrier existed, the U.S. Ordnance Department commenced work on this project in mid-1918. It was intended that the vehicle should be mass-produced by the Ford Motor Company (an output of 100 a day was planned) and so standard Ford automobile components were, as far as possible, introduced into the design.

A prototype was completed and tested in France in October with satisfactory results, because American G.H.Q. cabled from France to order 15,000. Various uses were proposed besides the original role of machine-gun carrier, including cargo carrier with 1500 lbs. capacity, self-propelled infantry howitzer and tractor, in emergency, for the 75-mm. field gun. The Armistice followed shortly afterwards, however, the big order was cancelled and only fifteen vehicles were completed.

The Ford 3-ton tank, as these little vehicles generally came to be known. weighed just under 3 tons (3·1 short tons), was 13 ft 8 in. long, 5 ft 6 in, wide and 5 ft 3 in. high. It owed some of its design layout to the Renault tank but it had no turret and the transmission system was entirely different from that of the French vehicle. Two Ford Model T engines were employed, each complete with its own electric starter, Ford planetary transmission (two speeds forward, one speed reverse), cardan shaft and worm driven half-axle. By varying the gear ratios for each engine, supplemented by the foot brakes when necessary, slow, fast or skid turns in either direction could be achieved. This system permitted easy manoeuvring, although controlling the two engines was not a simple task. The combined

horse power of the two four-cylinder water-cooled engines was forty-five and the maximum speed of the Ford 3-ton tank was 8 m.p.h.

The interior was cramped: the engines at the back, the driver sitting in the centre with the gunner in front of him. The armament as shown in the drawings consisted of one 0·30-in. machine-gun, which had only limited movement—21 degrees traverse and 38 degrees in the vertical plane. A simple ball mounting was at first provided for the gun but this was later changed to an armoured tube mounting resembling a gun of heavier calibre.

A larger three-man tank with a turret also built by the Ford Motor Co. appeared in 1918 but this was unsatisfactory in several ways and went no further than the prototype.

88 Autocanon Peugeot and Automitrailleuse Peugeot, 1918, France.

The Peugeot concern—S.A. des Automobiles et Cycles Peugeot—with its three factories was, with Renault, the earliest to produce armoured cars in France after the outbreak of the First World War. Some 18-h.p. Peugeot chassis were armoured by the Belgians in 1915 and the first armoured car for French use appears to have been built at about the same time. This was a conventional vehicle with the gun or machine-gun mounted with a shield near the rear of the hull. The engine bonnet (which may have been armoured only at the radiator end) was rounded in this model.

Later in the war an improved model of the 1915 type was produced. This was distinguished by a square, fully armoured engine compartment and wire-spoke wheels (dual at the rear) in place of the artillery wheels of the earlier model. Two types were produced. Automitrailleuse, with a Hotchkiss machine-gun and Autocanon with a 37-mm. gun. The latter was usually mounted in a deeper shield with a flat face, instead of the V-shaped shield of the machine-gun car. These armoured cars were usually operated in sections of three cars, two armed with machine-guns and one with the cannon.

Twenty-eight Peugeot armoured cars remained in French service at the end of the war and some were supplied to the Poles after the Russo-Polish War.

89 Leichter Kampfwagen II, 1918, Germany.

The Leichter Kampfwagen II was evolved directly from the L.K. I following experience with that machine which helped formulate official specifications and performance desiderata for a light tank.

Like its predecessor, the L.K. II was intended to make use of the available supply of redundant heavy motor car chassis without excessive modification and so the design was again forced into the front engine, rear crew compartment layout, with track drive from sprockets attached to the rear axles.

The two prototypes of L.K. II produced in the summer of 1918 by the Daimler firm were generally similar mechanically to the L.K. I but in place of the direct drive from the rear axles an extra gear train was introduced and a somewhat higher degree of accessibility for maintenance—particularly of the track system—was included. The arm-

our was thicker—14 mm. maximum— to resist close-range rifle fire (as stipulated) and the 'turret' was fixed, like that of the British Medium Mark A, which is believed to have influenced the design.

The armament was a 5·7-cm. gun, although a 3·7-cm. gun of higher velocity was intended for production models, some of which were alternatively to be armed with machine-guns only.

The L.K. II weighed about $8\frac{3}{4}$ tons— slightly over specified weight—and its length was 16 ft 8 in.—shorter than L.K. I, but sufficient to be able to cross a 6 ft 6 in. trench as laid down in the Kriegsministerium requirements. An order for 580 production vehicles was placed in June 1918 but the end of the war prevented the completion of any of these.

In order to overcome unsatisfactory features of the engine and transmission of L.K. II a new version, L.K. III, was designed which went even further away from the original concept of using a motor car chassis only slightly modified. In this the engine, a gear-box and final drive (which were entirely redesigned) were all concentrated in the rear, the fighting compartment being transferred to the front. The L.K. III would have supplanted L.K. II in production in 1919 but the Armistice put an end to these plans before even a prototype was built and subsequent work was prevented by the Treaty of Versailles.

Development of the L.K. II was, however, continued in Sweden where the designs were taken after the war. An improved version with a revolving turret, but in most respects very like the German prototype, was put into production for the Swedish Army from 1921 for several years onwards.

90 Tank, Mark IX, 1918, U.K.

The need for armoured cross-country troop and supply carriers was recognized when the first tanks were built. In practice this was carried out by standard or slightly modified heavy tanks—satisfactorily in the case of the supply carriers which were converted Tanks Marks I–IV or Gun Carriers, but very unsuccessfully for carrying men unaccustomed to travelling in the confined, poorly ventilated and rocking interior of a tank.

It was decided in 1917, therefore, to produce a tank specially as a supply or infantry carrier. The design was entrusted to Lieutenant G. J. Rackham: work was commenced in September and the prototype of Tank, Mark IX completed by Sir. W. G. Armstrong, Whitworth & Co. in the following year. Full-scale production (which was undertaken by Marshall Sons & Co. of Gainsborough, Lincolnshire) started too late for Mark IXs to be used in action, although thirty-five were completed by the end of 1918.

The Tank, Mark IX could carry up to fifty infantrymen or ten tons of supplies. The hull was an elongated version of the lozenge profile of the Mark V, etc. but without the sponsons, which were replaced by two large oval doors on each side. The fixed armament consisted only of two Hotchkiss machine-guns, but a row of loopholes was provided on each side of the hull to allow infantry being carried to use their own light weapons.

Mechanically, the Mark IX was based on the Mark V. In order to give a large clear space in the middle of the tank, the Ricardo 150-h.p. engine was placed immediately behind the driver's/commander's compartment although the gear-box and, of course, final drive was at the rear of the tank. This left the centre compartment (13 ft 6 in. long and 5 ft 3 in. wide) clear except for the cardan shaft running through the centre.

The Mark IX had a loaded weight of 37 tons and the same engine as the Mark V so, not surprisingly, the top speed was low (only 4 m.p.h.) compared with contemporary British heavy tanks. However, it would have played a useful part had the war continued longer and development of this type of machine—which was neglected for the next twenty years—would have been followed.

An experimental amphibious version of the Mark IX, fitted with long cylindrical air drums each side, was first tried out on the Welsh Harp at Hendon, near London, on Armistice Day, 1918.

91 Self-Propelled Caterpillar Mounts, Mark I and Mark III, 1918, U.S.A.

A series of experimental self-propelled tracked mountings for heavy artillery was built in the United States between 1918 and 1921. The earliest of these were either based fairly closely on French designs or were, in some cases, almost exact copies of the French originals and the weapons mounted were usually Schneider long-range guns or heavy howitzers.

These vehicles were designated 'Self-Propelled Caterpillar Mounts' because the chassis were actual Holt Caterpillar designs or in the case of the French prototypes were derived from them. Both the Schneider and Saint-Chamond tanks and self-propelled artillery chassis were based on U.S. Holt Caterpillar tractors.

The Self-Propelled Caterpillar Mount Mark I mounted the 8 in. (203·2 mm.) howitzer. This had normal elevation but only very limited traverse was available, once the vehicle was positioned. A small crew was carried to handle the shells for the howitzer.

The S.P.C.M. Mark III was for the 240-mm. Schneider howitzer: it was a much larger vehicle for the heavier weapon, which was centrally mounted and had only a slight amount of traverse.

The United States Army abandoned development of these heavy self-propelled mountings during the 1920s when the emphasis came to be placed on the mobility of lighter weapons and it was not revived until 1943–44, during the Second World War.

92 Tank, Medium, Mark B, 1918, U.K.

The Medium Mark A, which successfully demonstrated the value of this class of tank, had a number of shortcomings, the principal of which was the difficulty of handling. The Medium Mark B was designed to overcome this fault and at the same time incorporate other features which by 1918 the considerable experience of the Tank Corps in action showed were desirable.

The lozenge-shaped silhouette of the heavy tanks was adopted—perhaps from conservatism in Major W. G. Wilson the designer, because it was not strictly necessary. The main part of the

armament was, however, carried in a rectangular superstructure raised above the top line of the track and fitted with five ball mountings for Hotchkiss machine-guns. Advantage was taken of the high hull to include a form of sponson with one ball mounting on the door each side. A 'male' version of the Medium Mark 'B' was also planned, with a 2-pdr. gun included in the armament, but none of these were built.

The engine used was a four-cylinder Ricardo—a smaller edition of that designed for the heavy Tank, Mark V. It was placed somewhat further back than in earlier tanks and left rather more room for the crew compartment at the front. This engine, linked with a four-speed epicyclic gear-box made the machine relatively easy to control, but it was underpowered for a tank weighing 18 tons and the top speed of 6 m.p.h. was not considered good enough for a medium.

A new feature in this tank was a means of producing a smoke screen by introducing sulphonic acid into the engine exhaust.

The initial order for Medium Mark B's was increased to 450 in the Summer of 1918 but the end of the war brought about a cancellation of the order after only forty-five tanks had been completed by the Metropolitan Carriage, Wagon & Finance Co. and the North British Locomotive Co. The Armistice occurred before there was time to train and equip units of the Tank Corps to use the Medium Mark B in action but some were sent to Russia with the British expedition in 1919 and others to Ireland in the same year. The Medium Mark B's performance was inferior to that of the Mark C and so was not used to equip the Tanks Corps after 1919 except that some were used for training at the Bovington Depot for a few years.

93 Tank, Mark V**, 1918, U.K.

The Tank Mark V** was a fundamental redesign by Major W. G. Wilson of his basic Mark V to produce the same trench-crossing ability as the Mark V* but at the same time to introduce improvements and eliminate the faults which had shown up in trials of the earlier machine.

The overall length of the Mark V** was identical to that of the Mark V*— 32 ft 5 in.—and the gap it could span was also about 14 ft. The general appearance was also much the same, although the chief external difference— the commander's fixed turret immediately behind and raised above the driver's position—gave the clue to the main feature of the internal rearrangement. The engine was placed further back, permitting the command turret to be brought forward and also improving the balance and the transmission arrangement.

The engine used was a six-cylinder Ricardo but uprated to produce 225 h.p. and this gave a better top speed of 5·2 m.p.h. Handling qualities, compared with Mark V*, were also improved as a result of the better balance and a redesign of the hull contour which, among other things, gave about 6 in. longer track contact with the ground. The ventilation system was rearranged and the grilles in the hull sides, characteristic of Marks V and V*, were eliminated.

Large orders for Tanks, Mark V** were cancelled at the end of the war and, after the Armistice, only a few were completed in 1918–1919. These were used for several years after the war for various experiments with equipment such as tank bridges.

94 Tank, Mark V** Bridgelayer, 1918, U.K.

During the battles leading up to the Armistice in 1918, the German Army made extensive use of natural obstacles, such as small rivers and canals, as defence against advance by British tanks. This situation had, in fact, been anticipated by the Tank Corps General Staff by the end of 1917 and in the early part of the following year an experimental bridge to cross a 20-ft gap—the extent of most of the lesser water obstacles— was designed and built by Tank Corps workshops. The workshops in France were unable to construct tank bridges in the numbers required and the Director of Fortifications and Works at the War Office was asked to help. Major C. E. Inglis, Royal Engineers, was sent out to France and after discussion of the problems with the Tank Corps staff, recommended that three types of bridge should be constructed for tank use—a heavy pontoon bridge for crossing rivers wider than 100 ft; a tubular bridge suitable for gaps up to 100 ft; and a bridge carried by tanks for gaps up to 20 ft.

Three Bridging Battalions, R.E. were formed just before the Armistice, although the end of the war resulted in their disbandment, leaving only a Company to carry out post-war experiments.

The 20-ft tank bridge of the type that would have been used in action is shown in the drawings, carried by a

Tank, Mark V★★. It is hinged at the front of the vehicle and is raised and lowered by means of a mechanical winch located behind the driver's cab. The whole operation of bridging a 20-ft gap took only two minutes. Experiments with this type of equipment were carried on for several years after the war with the 'R.E. Tank'.

95 Carro Fiat Tipo 2000, 1918, Italy.

A French Schneider tank was acquired by Italy in 1917 and it was at first proposed that copies of this vehicle should be manufactured in Italy for the Italian Army. This scheme proved to be impracticable for various reasons and encouragement was given to the Fiat company, of Turin, to continue the design of a heavy tank, which they had already begun, and authority for the construction of two prototype vehicles.

The Fiat company had no previous experience in tracklaying vehicles and the two tanks—Carro Armato Fiat Tipo 2000—were not completed until near the end of 1918.

Approximately the same length as the British Mark IV tank, the Fiat was rather more roomy inside because of the taller hull, surmounted by a revolving turret. This was the first heavy tank, in fact, to mount a cannon-armed turret: this layout had been rejected by the British, French and German designers because it pushed upwards the centre of gravity. In addition to the 65-mm. gun in the turret, seven mountings for Revelli machine-guns were provided in the hull—one at each corner, one each side and one in the centre of the rear plate. Because the engine (at

the rear) was decked over inside the hull access from one end of the tank to the other was possible for the crew. The tank was manned by ten men, including eight gunners. The driver at the front was provided with a periscope for normal vision.

A Fiat six-cylinder water-cooled engine of 240 h.p. powered the tank and produced a maximum speed of only $4\frac{1}{2}$ m.p.h., although the vehicle was rather heavy at 40 tons. The suspension consisted of ten road wheels each side, eight of them grouped in pairs in bogey units sprung on leaf springs.

Only the two tanks originally ordered were built—the second of these differed in details, including a flat-topped turret instead of the dome-shaped one in the first model, illustrated here.

96 Tank, Medium, Mark C, 1918, U.K.

Destined to be the mainstay of the post-war Tank Corps for several years, the Medium Mark C was designed in December 1917 but production was too late for any of these tanks to take part in the war. Sir William Tritton's design was approved on 19 April 1918, and later an initial 200 Medium Mark Cs were ordered, with the idea that they would play a leading part in the exploitation of the break-through of the German line planned for 1919. The Armistice intervened, however, when thirty-six tanks were nearly completed by William Foster & Co Ltd. at Lincoln. These vehicles were completed, together with a few more at the works of Armlet & Wortley of Leeds, and were subsequently issued to the Tank Corps.

Tritton was able to bring to the design of the Medium Mark C his wide experience of earlier tanks including the Medium Mark A, together with information gained from officers of the Tank Corps based on their experience in action. The Medium Mark C, although bearing a later designation, was in fact a contemporary of Major W. G. Wilson's Medium Mark B, but it avoided the main faults of that tank and was, in many ways, one of the best wartime designs. For one thing the standard six-cylinder Ricardo engine (as fitted in the heavy Tanks, Marks V, VII and IX) was used and in a $19\frac{1}{2}$-ton tank produced a fair power/weight ratio representing a speed of nearly 8 m.p.h.

A male version of the tank with a 6-pdr. gun was planned, but none were built and all of those that were were 'females', armed with four Hotchkiss machine-guns. Detail refinements—many of them suggested by battlefield experience—included improved stowage arrangements for the crew's equipment and spare parts for the vehicle and provision for an anti-aircraft mounting for a machine-gun. For the first time the tank commander was given a revolving cupola, mounted on the top of the fixed turret.

Medium Mark Cs were seen around for several years after the war until by 1925 most had been replaced in the Tank Corps by Vickers Light Tanks (later known as Mediums). Even as late as 1931, however, there was a proposal to modify the Medium Mark C as a Salvage Tank although, not surprisingly, this idea was not accepted.

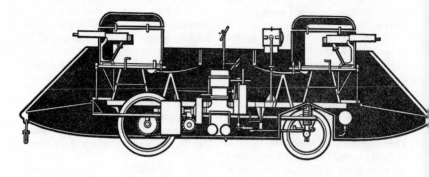

Fig. 1   Simms Motor War Car, 1902, U.K.—length 28 ft

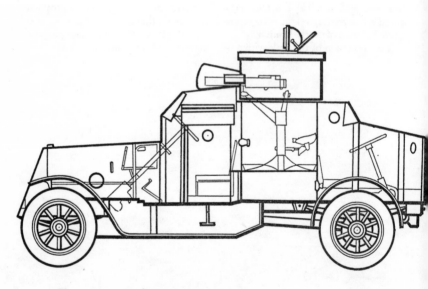

Fig. 2   Armoured Car, Austin (1917–18 pattern), U.K.—length 16 ft

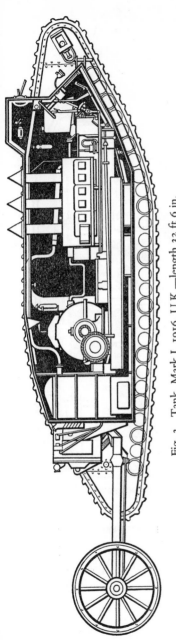

Fig. 3   Tank, Mark I, 1916, U.K.—length 32 ft 6 in.

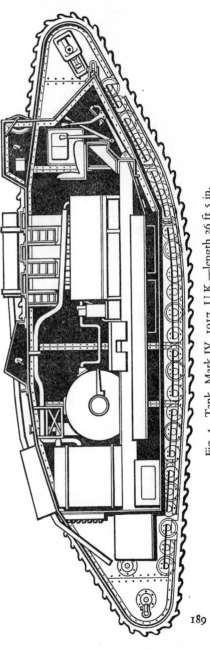

Fig. 4   Tank, Mark IV, 1917, U.K.—length 26 ft 5 in.

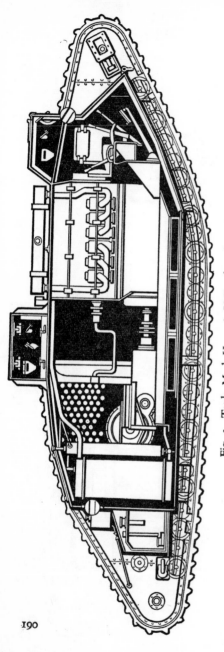

Fig. 5 Tank, Mark V, 1918, U.K.—length 26 ft 5 in.

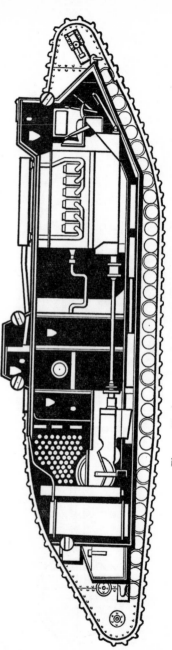

Fig. 6 Tank, Mark V*, 1918, U.K.—length 32 ft 5 in.

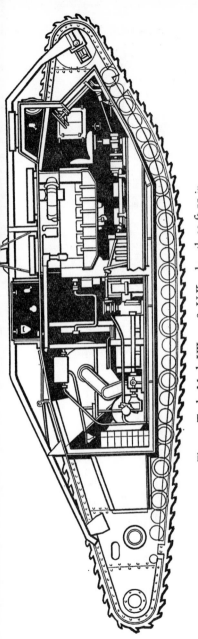

Fig. 7   Tank, Mark VII, 1918, U.K.—length 29 ft 11 in.

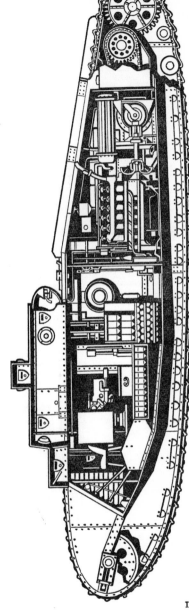

Fig. 8   Tank, Mark VIII, 1918, U.K./U.S.A.—length 34 ft 2½ in.

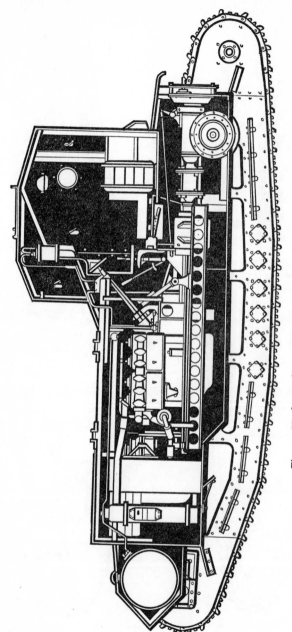

Fig. 9 Tank, Medium, Mark A, 1917, U.K.—length 20 ft

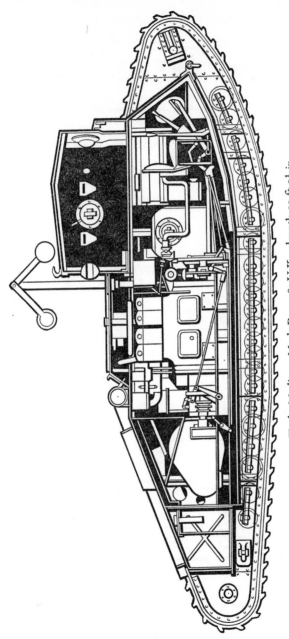

Fig. 10 Tank, Medium, Mark B, 1918, U.K.—length 22 ft $9\frac{1}{2}$ in.

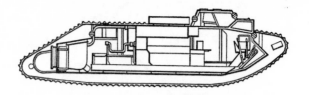

Fig. 11   Tank, Mark V**, 1918, U.K.—length 32 ft 5 in.

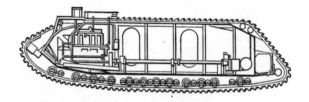

Fig. 12   Tank, Mark IX, 1918, U.K.—length 31 ft 10 in.

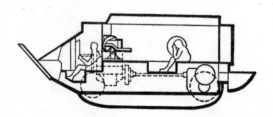

Fig. 13   Char Schneider, 1916, France—length 19 ft 8 in.

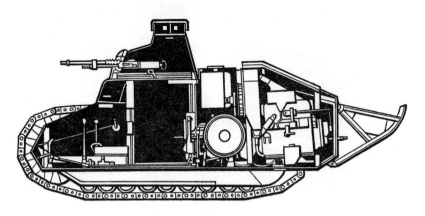

Fig. 14   Char Renault FT 17, 1917, France—length 16 ft 5 in.

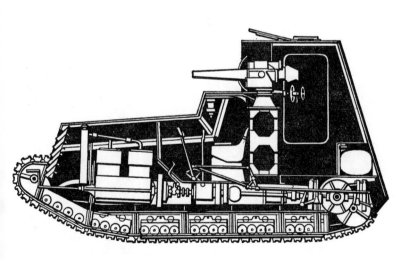

Fig. 15   Leichter Kampfwagen II, 1918, Germany—length 16 ft 8 in.

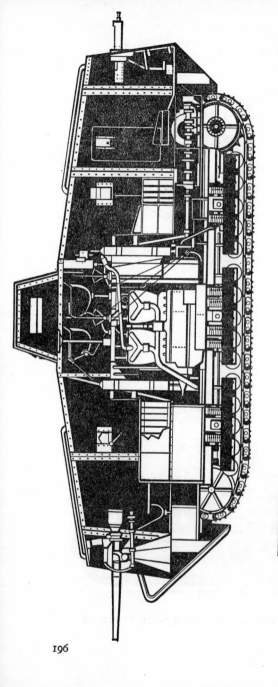

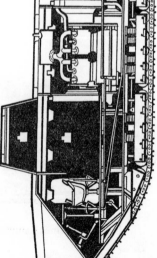

Fig. 16   Schwerer Kampfwagen A7V, 1917, Germany—length 26 ft 3 in overall.

(This drawing shows a nose skid which was not included in production vehicles.)

Fig. 17   Schwerer Kampfwagen A7V/U, 1918, Germany—length 27 ft 6 in.

INDEX